The Regime

Patients Behind Bars

Sandra Paterson

Published in 2015
with the help of Lumphanan Press
9 Anderson Terrace, Tarland,
Aberdeenshire, AB34 4YH
www.lumphananpress.co.uk

ISBN: 978-0-9927468-7-2

Printed and bound by Imprint Digital,
Upton Pyne, Devon, UK.

Proceeds from this book will go towards Aberdeen Life Coaching:
www.aberdeenlifecoaching.com

For the blessing of my boys and their wives: Marc, Stuart, Richie, Ewen, Lisa, and Colleen; my grandaughter Jasmine; my family and friends for their encouragement; Denis for his love.

Thanks to all the guys who shared their personal stories and helped with the title of this book. God bless you all and may you all choose a healthier path.

To nurses and health workers around the world, and to my readers: love and gratitude.

Contents

Foreword

We all have birth mothers and fathers, we are all born into families and communities with their own set regime, and we all depend on the National Health Service (NHS).

This book is not a medical journal, nor do I claim to be a professional writer. The purpose of this book is to send an SOS to as many people as possible in an attempt to help 'save our service', 'save our spirit', and 'save our soul' from disease. I have written it to share my own thoughts and observations on how we can, and must, all get involved if we are to save our NHS from total collapse, to save our spirit from depression and save our soul from disease. We have a fast-growing, overwhelming, demand on the NHS and the system is not coping. I believe we all appreciate that our NHS is one of the world's leading health care providers and therefore worth saving. My ultimate aim is to do my bit, however small, to help people find a way to believe more in themselves and protect themselves.

I will share some of my own personal stories and experience

of 40 years in nursing and, by sharing a little of my own journey in life, will hopefully trigger something that gets you thinking about what you could do to enhance your own health or support the wellbeing of others. I aim to encourage people to be true to themselves, as I have been to myself when writing this book. I truly believe we are all on a path that was planned before we were born; what has happened to us was meant to have happened to us. Whatever happened in the past has gone and whatever happens next is what counts. It's important to look back at past experience and accept it as something to learn from, something that has made you the person you are today. Tomorrow can be different if you choose it to be – it could be the start of a new, healthier, mind game that's better for all of us.

I will point you in the direction of other books that you may find interesting and encouraging, and hopefully guide you towards knowing your inner body as well as your outer body, helping you to take charge of your own health and happiness. I aim to reach as many readers as possible and, being aware of the differences in people's learning skills, I have included a poem at the end of the text and many analogies throughout it. I plan to speak to you as if we were sitting in a café having a chat. Hopefully my humour will not offend my audience!

Introduction

Every human on this earth today and before us has required the help of someone at some time, either to support them emotionally, physically, mentally or spiritually.

Our health services are little different to other industries around the globe who admit they are struggling to survive, and we hear regularly through the media that the NHS is not coping. The foundations of the NHS have been on solid ground since 1948; however, recently the system, as well its staff, have begun to feel the pressure. More and more people demand our attention but don't listen to our advice. General Practitioners (GPs) give out prescriptions but many patients do not follow through the treatment. Some even share their prescribed medication with others, while some just don't take their health and wellbeing seriously enough. It often seems we are expected to have a magic wand that will fix them.

NHS providers are not robots and they get ill just like everyone else, becoming sick with the stress and demands put upon them. Crumbling at the seams, our present system is heading for total collapse. You could say that the NHS is terminally ill, in emotional turmoil and distress. Experienced nurses with valuable years of wisdom and experience, full of compassion, are being forced to give up due to the stress of their workload, which takes a heavy toll on their health. Doctors are being flown in from other countries just to prevent our NHS doors from closing, while our own doctors are exhausted due to bureaucracy and an overwhelming need for repetitive documentation (a major factor in the amount of time wasted in the NHS). We are being pulled away from what matters the most: time for assessment and treatment, with compassion being the main healing agent.

The NHS doesn't have enough experienced staff to deal with patients' complex needs; we have limited hospital beds for the frail elderly to fully recover in and very few rooms available in our nursing homes. People are sent home from hospital just to be re-admitted the next day, sometimes even though it means a 40-mile round journey.

I'm sure most would agree that the NHS is far from perfect these days. However, most would disagree on the cause of the problem. Some say it's the government's fault for not providing the funds to pay staff, some would blame Health and Safety for introducing time consuming and awkward policies. Or is it a lack of communication between doctors, nurses, patients, and relatives? I would argue that no one person or strategy is at fault and that, in fact, to some extent we are all to blame.

I'm sure those who argue that health and safety policies are to blame for sapping resources would agree that there would not be such demands if everyone took more care to be self-responsible. Accidents do happen – we are all guilty for that

– and policies are required to stamp out negligence. It seems people are quick to sue and claim money these days, giving no thought or consideration to the cost and damage to the NHS budget and service.

Some people argue that our society has become selfish, materialistic, irresponsible and disrespectful to others as well as ourselves; we are so ashamed of ourselves that we look to blame someone else. Personally, I think there may be some truth in that, and it may have a negative impact on our general health and wellbeing.

Someone I was involved with told me she had requested an operation to have her stomach clamped and was very disappointed to be refused surgery by medical staff. The medical staff suggested she should try to lose some weight before they could make a clear decision, due to the invasive nature of the surgery. This person then took action and went to get personal help to lose weight for the operation. However, she was so pleased with herself for taking action and losing weight that in the end she did not require the surgery. She then went on to say she had saved the health board a lot of money!

What surprised me was her attitude towards the health board. It was clear that she was able with support to reduce her weight, which was a great personal achievement for her.

In my grandparents' and great grandparents' day people died from a range of incurable acute infections. Infectious diseases would have been a main cause of worry for parents about their children. Bugs such as diphtheria, tetanus, measles, whooping cough and pneumonia were some of the well-known diseases responsible for loss of life in babies and toddlers; for mothers it would have been postpartum sepsis (blood infection) after childbirth. It was all too common for adults to die from chest and throat infections, which was then believed to have caused heart failure. Many patients who developed infected leg ulcers would routinely be victims of early amputation. That was before the birth of antibiotics, and happily such diseases are no longer thought of as deadly.

The NHS was set up for people who required medical intervention for things they had no control over, people requiring lifesaving operations due to infectious diseases or perhaps accidents; it was not set up as the quick-fix service that it has now become. However, it is very clear that many people nowadays are unable to look after themselves properly. It is also clear that we should be spending money to prevent the need for surgery in the first place. It is also very clear that what we are currently doing is not working.

We now rely heavily on the NHS for the care and support of a whole new world of ill health: chronic diseases. Unlike infectious diseases that are cured with antibiotics, chronic diseases cannot be treated so easily. Chronic illness grows worse, is ongoing, and the best anyone can expect is remission with recurring episodes of pain and discomfort. It becomes part of life. A disease in one area of the body may put pressure on other parts of the body and cause widespread dysfunction. Chronic diseases familiar to the general public include heart disease, dementia, depression, asthma, obstructive pulmonary disease, kidney and liver disease, cancer, and inflammatory diseases such as fibromyalgia and chronic fatigue.

We may live longer these days, but we don't always do so with the freedom of good health. We need an updated, functional method of assessment. Inside our bodies are many systems; if they are not in harmony we have problems. A more functional model of health prevention and intervention, based on the individual, would be a great step in treating these illnesses. Not only would we see a decline in chronic illness rates, but in crime also. Our inner bodies are no different from systems of the environment – if we don't all work in harmony we have chaos in society.

Our current culture creates a huge amount of stress that many of us don't seem to be coping with. Some of us are in the wrong job and don't even know it till we attend the GP with stress-related symptoms such as backache, headache, memory loss or lack of concentration. Stress and anxiety can even cause biological changes. High blood pressure, heart problems, stroke and diabetes are very common nowadays. Instead of simply taking the treatment given by the doctor it is worth thinking about the causes of these problems in the first place; labels are only symptoms of something gone wrong on the outside that has caused the inside of your body to change. Sadly, by just carrying on with life without more thought, these problems will only increase and lead to secondary illness.

Men, woman and children struggle with their mental health. Our children are being emotionally destroyed through fear, bullying and the way they are spoken down to. Young men find themselves locked up in prisons (many due to emotional distress), some of our elderly turn to alcohol because they are isolated and lonely, and the NHS is struggling to keep up with the demand. As the years go past more and more sick or mentally ill casualties flood in expecting the NHS to fix them.

Is it not time to wake up and take a good look at what is going on around us? Or do we need to wait for scientific proof? People are changing just as fast as the seasons and the weather, and we are all in trouble. We have all invested in our hospitals and communities, the elderly having worked and lived through wars to do so. And for what? Why are more and more people suffering from chronic health problems? I believe we will end up needing to build more mental health hospitals or prisons if we don't all take charge of our own health and welfare, and support others.

We have become a nation of quick-fix food and quick-fix medication; we all seem to be in such a hurry to have things now and we get frustrated when we have to wait. Pharmaceutical companies are profit-driven industries more interested in their business model than any human model. Everything seems to be about increasing profit and decreasing expenses. Patients only have ten minutes per visit with their GP, and unless they can communicate their symptoms effectively in that time it may well take months to get to the bottom of an illness.

With such a short time to speak to their GP, is it any wonder that people come out of the surgery no more the wiser about what to do than when they first went in? I have heard some people confess that they just don't feel comfortable when speaking to a doctor as they can't find the correct words to describe how they actually feel. Some people even feel anxious and afraid of what the doctor may say or discover about them. The attitude of some doctors doesn't help either. I've heard of GPs who start typing out prescriptions before a patient has even had a chance to finish what they want to say, which isn't acceptable patient care. However, it is perhaps not surprising given the time and pressure our doctors are constantly under. This is the type of thing that stops people attending the GP as it leaves them with a feeling of unimportance. We can all imagine how tough it must be anyway to attend a GP for emotional issues, opening up to someone you don't know, fearing that you might burst into tears, feeling guilty for taking up too much time.

Our country is supposed to support freedom of choice, but people don't consider the consequences of their actions. If we choose not to work then we choose to be broke. If we choose to eat rubbish then we choose to feel like rubbish. If we choose to drink and take drugs then we choose the consequences. If we choose to lie, cheat or steal then we choose to be punished. Nowadays there are so many organisations available for us to choose the help we need, so what's really gone wrong? Most of us have the ability to help ourselves and others with the assistance of services from voluntary organisations, which are perhaps not recognised or valued enough for their contribution and dedication. The voluntary sector provides the kindness and compassion we desperately need if we are to sustain our health and wellbeing in the future, and they do seem to be ahead of the game when it comes to supporting people in our fast-changing world.

Of course I realise that there are many people, both young and old, who for genuine reasons are not aware that they could access help for their problems. However, if the walking well could just get themselves to the chemist instead of the GP for their initial advice then it would free up GPs to give the less fortunate more time to diagnose their problems.

An important first step towards solving some of the problems in the system would be for for the government to stop using the NHS as bait during election campaigns, and to save the NHS from total privatisation. However, the most important thing we can do is to change the way we think about what causes chronic diseases. As I mentioned before, do we honestly need to wait for more scientific proof to decide what is making us ill? It is abundantly clear that the present system of health care is not working, and that preventing illness must surely be as cost effective as curing illness. Our focus at the moment is on saving people who have fallen to disease or become vulnerable. We need to focus more on the causes of illness and prevention in the first place.

I work closely with senior citizens who often tell me that they are sick of hearing in the media that they cost the country a fortune because they are living longer. Many already feel guilty as they witness young family members die before them from depression or drug and alcohol misuse. A great many grannies are bringing up children from the second generation due to unfit parenting. Our older population not only suffer from debilitating illness but also mental stress due to our modern way of living, suffering from isolation and dissociation due to the modern technology that causes chronic disconnection with other human beings (like, for example, having to wait forever on the telephone just to hear music play, while being told by an electronic voice to either hold or phone back later).

I have also seen patients with symptoms of pseudo-dementia. Pseudo-dementia is not permanent, it is caused by a depression that affects your ability to think clearly and can cause difficulty in making decisions, or problems concentrating. When treated, these symptoms will go away.

Community nurses witness vulnerable patients who have been subject to lifelong physical and emotional abuse from their partners. We are now engaging with others who have silently suffered a generation of verbal aggression and bullying, causing deep emotional distress that also affects the health of their extended families.

Many of today's illnesses stem from our own emotional problems and distorted belief systems, as well as our negative reactions to things that have happened in our past or things currently happening that cause ill feelings. Cardiovascular ill health, poor digestion, and wound healing are just some physiological examples that can be affected by our emotional state of mind

Our parents and members of past generations perhaps did not help our relationship with our emotions. Have you ever been told in the past, 'Be big and don't cry,' or 'It's only girls that cry,' or 'No use crying over spilled milk'? They may have believed it was the correct thing to do at the time, and it was what they were taught as children after all, but times have changed and we now recognise the need to have a more direct connection with our emotions.

Emotional pain, if not corrected, will lead to physical pain, and feeling physical pain will be the trigger that alerts you to seek help. A doctor may provide the pill to fix you, but for many people the pills only reduce the inflammation for a short time, covering up the symptoms. The true cause will carry on undetected until you are honest enough and strong enough to take a look at your lifestyle and make the necessary changes to your habits. I am a strong believer that patients need to be seen in a holistic manor and not just as person X with a mechanical, physical problem. There is more to ill health than physical illness.

There is a whole world of corruption and dysfunction going on inside our bodies and toxic messages seep through from the outside due to our behaviour and environment. We are facing an epidemic of childhood emotional trauma, which is reflected in some of the diseases of today. We must all band together to prevent this epidemic of disease, as we all have the power within us to stay healthy.

The future of our NHS depends on us all, and we can't save it without the help of each individual member of the public. Haven't we all, at some time, depended on the support of the NHS for the care and repair of our outer and inner selves? The thing is that we have got to the stage where we take for granted the fact that the NHS will always be there, and it's led to us not making an effort to take care of ourselves properly.

I agree with many of today's scientists and firmly believe their theories that we need to look at new methods of preventative treatment. I am impressed by how many scientists believe that we can change our general health and wellbeing in the long-term through an intensive regime of personalised management involving mindfulness and meditation. This has has been proved to improve emotional and physical function. It may seem to be costly in time, but financially the time will prove to be cost effective. Is it not time we all invested in ourselves instead of waiting to fall victim to some chronic illness?

The focus of care in the future will be provided by the Health and Social Partnership, which is almost at the implementation stages and will soon be up and running. These joint services will provide individuals with the holistic, patient-centered care that they need, providing a wider range of family and community support networks within a one-team approach.

Alternative therapies also provide great support to health services, which gives the public yet more choice. Kindness and compassion has been scientifically proven to be effective and beneficial in healing and maintaining our body functions. I strongly feel the subject should be taught in schools, where we need to start if we are to encourage healthy human beings in the future. Supporting emotional wellbeing should be high on the agenda in all industries and workplaces.

Everyone can participate in helping others, and if everyone focuses on showing understanding and kindness then, like medical staff, everyone will be able to save a life or add hope to someone's holistic wellbeing. Let's all make it our responsibility to try to see things from a different perspective, to be responsible and to help prevent unnecessary pill popping and needless trips to the GP. Our children are the ones that will suffer if we don't come together and do our bit.

It is my belief that if we can end emotional abuse our children will stand a chance to transform this world into a peaceful, tranquil place that is free from disease.

Chapter 1

My story begins

*"Life is like being at the funfair – we always
look ahead to the next ride and miss out on fully
experiencing the one we are on."*

My birth was breaking news for my family and their friends, and for the wider population three days before my birth United Kingdom's first ever motorway, the Preston bypass, was opened by Prime Minister Harold MacMillan. It was the year Connie Francis had three chart hits, 'Stupid Cupid', 'Who's Sorry Now', and 'I'm Sorry I Made You Cry'.

Toilet paper was a luxury.

Toothpaste appeared in a tin: *Gibbs*.

Omo, *Tide* and *Fairy* were the popular choices in washing powder.

The Red Letter, *People's Friend* and *Family Star* were the favoured magazines, along with the *Beano, Dandy* and the *Bunty*, not to forget the *Oor Wullie* and the *Broons*.

BBC produced the *Black and White Minstrel* show, *Blue Peter* and *Grandstand*. ITV were offering *Ivanhoe*, *The Invisible Man*, and *The Adventures of William Tell*.

Children of all ages favoured *Watch with Mother, Andy Pandy,*

Rag Tag and Bobtail, Picture Book, Take Your Pick, Dixon of Dock Green, Crackerjack and *Opportunity Knocks.*

The same year saw the end of the *Flower Pot Men, Woodentops, Living it Up* and *Six-Five Special,* not to mention the sad end of Gareth Jones, known for *Armchair Theatre,* who died off-stage during his performance.

The 11-plus test had been introduced around the time of my birth, an exam dreaded by all 11-year-olds. It determined everyone's future path in education. It's true to say I hadn't a clue.

A Brief Personal History

On a Tuesday in December 1958, just after midnight, I saw the light after nine whole months of personal development. I finally pushed my way out from the warm, dark place of my growth into the unknown to be greeted with a slap and a smile from a satisfied midwife, swiftly followed by the exhausted voice of my mother, 'Never again!' I was not aware that I had just burst out of my cocoon, like a caterpillar that turns into butterfly.

With the lifeline to my mother cut there was no return. I was now an individual human being about to begin my own life. My mind was a blank page, unaware of my thoughts. I was just "I" and I didn't even know it, my whole being alive and surviving without my knowledge. My lungs knew what to do, my heart pumped away, my legs and arms kicked. I could scream and wet myself but thoughts and beliefs did not exist. I was a living puppet waiting to be programmed by other human beings, waiting like a computer for data input from sources outwith myself.

My home back in late fifties and sixties was a little two-roomed house that we Scots know as a But n' Ben. The cottage rented to my grandmother was at number 5 Bullers o' Buchan near Cruden Bay, Aberdeenshire. In 1958, my mother, sister and grandmother all squeezed into the small house as we waited for our own home to be allocated to us. There was no running water to the house so we toiled with carrying fresh water from a spring well. The water in the well came from a small pipe buried deep underground and sprang from a spout on an embankment half-way down a rocky cliff. We used a metal bucket to collect the water directly from the pipe and carried it up to the house.

For light in the evenings we used a paraffin wick lamp called a *Tilly* or sometimes had to rely on candles, as there was no electricity. Our toilet was called the can or lav, and was in a hut the width of a telephone kiosk and around four feet high, out the back of the house. It consisted of a wooden rectangular board held up at each end with wooden supports. A large hole was cut out of the middle of the board, and a bucket placed underneath to catch the contents of all who sat on it. I seem to remember small pieces of newspaper lying at the side of the board, as toilet paper was not available to us back then. That was deemed a luxury!

I remember a cast-iron kettle sitting on the coal-fuelled stove with its noisy whistle constantly bellowing as it was almost always boiling. Bathing was once a week in a tin bath in front of the fire. We all took turns, one after the other, topping it up with boiling water from the kettle. There we had it all, our human needs met: water, food, plenty of fresh air, shelter, warmth and love.

Our house was set a few yards from the edge of some very

steep cliffs. You could always hear the seagulls squawking; they seemed to be saying, 'Take care, take care' as they nested in the cliff tops protecting their young. I remember the smell and taste of the salty sea air and the shiny slippery seaweed on the shore below. I remember that if I dared to go too close to the edge of the cliff on a stormy day I could witness the frothy water, looking like sheep's wool. The foam flew around at the bottom by the shoreline. I would hear the North Sea roaring as the big waves came in, lashing against the cliffs, retreating out of the many deep caves. It was eerie on a dark night, tucked up in bed, listening to the howling wind and rain lash against our single-pane glass windows, gusts rattling down the chimney pots.

In the summer it was glorious: the scent of the wild flowers as they blended with the sea air, everything so fresh and bright. The flowers would pop up in spring, covering the rugged rocks with snowdrops, crocus and daffodils. There would be colour almost all year round with many unusual wild flowers. Numerous walkers and tourists visited our little hamlet because the area was steeped in history. They followed the coastal walks that ran south to the impressive ruins of Slain's Castle which, perched on the edge of a steep descent down to the bottomless sea, was the inspiration for the famous Dracula tales. Sadly it was also notorious for many local tragedies, as adults and small children often slipped and fell from the edge of those cliffs. North from Bullers o' Buchan, the coastal path would take you to the small town of Boddam, passing what we called the Pot. This was a massive blow hole, formed over many years as the stormy northern sea carved a masterpiece of arches and caves from the granite rock which, I am told, were used by smugglers centuries ago. More recently German soldiers came ashore there during the war and were captured climbing the cliffs.

My first few years at this haven was a great adventure. I can't remember ever being told not to climb the rocks or to stay away from the edge of the path, or not to go near the water. We children could tell the dangers below and had the freedom to explore. I can only remember being called on by my folks when it was time to go inside for food or bed.

Progression and civilisation was on the horizon when a Shore Porter's removal van appeared one day at our house. It was time to move from our little But n' Ben, which had been my home for the best part of four years. My mother, sister and I were to be re-homed into a council flat in Bridge of Don just north of Aberdeen, while my gran stayed behind happily living the life she was used to. She wasn't looking to change her way of life.

I can't remember very much about the day we moved but I do remember having to sleep for some time on top of a mattress and a few scattered rugs my gran made from pieces of coloured cloth and potato sacks, on the linoleum-covered floor. We had very little furniture and stored our clothes in old tea chests and suitcases. Our new home was in a flat in a block of six and we had to hike to the top floor. The view from the front room was of tall woodland trees and you could spot in the distance the little croft houses scattered as far as the eye could see. Although we were miles away from rugged cliffs and the noise of the seagulls on the rocks, we could still see the clear blue sky and nesting birds in the trees. The rooms were far bigger than those in the little But n' Ben. We shared a balcony at the front of the block but we had our own balcony at the back. We shared a drying green downstairs and we had a little plot of allocated ground where we grew vegetables and some seasonal flowers.

An open coal fire provided the heating; the coal cellar was on the landing and to fill it up took four bags at a time. The poor man delivering coal had to carry four sacks up four flights of stairs. What would Health and Safety have to say about that today? We were also very lucky to have an indoor cycle shed at the bottom of the block of flats, although it would be some time before the cellar would be home to a bicycle of mine as such luxuries were never on the list of priorities.

Like all children of the sixties and seventies, we were fed and then sent out to play. Of course it was much safer back then. Few people could afford cars. If they were fortunate enough to own one, it was almost always on ramps with someone's dad underneath fixing something with spare bits from the scrap yard. We didn't need to wander far from the front door to find something interesting to do. There was always someone outside to play with, some neighbouring child to hop, skip and jump with, groups of girls playing with their dolls and prams, groups of boys playing endless games of football. Occasionally we went to the park some streets away to play on the swings and roundabouts, but often you had to wait your turn, as the parks were very busy and full of children. I remember there being a very tall chute that seemed to be the hub of the playground, with gangs of kids clambering and sliding down the poles like a fireman's pole rather than sliding down the chute itself.

Just before I entered my first year at school I developed tonsillitis and was taken into hospital to have surgery. Having your tonsils and adenoids removed was a common procedure in those days. The ward was a mixed ward of boys and girls. I remember the nurses bathing us two at a time the night before our operation. The day after the operation we were offered ice-cream but only if we ate our toast first. We were told the toast was to clear any dry blood remaining in our throat after the surgery. I also clearly remember the Ward Sister in her white hat standing tall at the bottom of the bed and asking us our names. The first boy to be asked was called George but I was surprised to hear that the second and third child said their name was also George, even though the second child was a girl. The Sister continued to go to each of the beds on the small ward and everyone said their name was George. She stood at the bottom of my bed and said 'And I suppose your name is also George?' I looked towards the others, who were smiling and nodding. They were much older than me so I smiled at the Sister and said in my most confident voice, 'Yip, I'm George.' Everyone was in fits of laughter – everyone except Sister, of course! That was my lasting memory of my first experience in a hospital.

In the street where I lived the children all seemed to live by a similar regime: get up, eat breakfast, then clean our teeth using the notorious *Gibbs* toothpaste. It came in a small round tin about the size of boot polish. We would run the toothbrush over the solid paste before scraping it up and down our teeth, top to bottom, both rows. I can still see the horrid pink chalky stuff, wet and full of brush marks from the person who had used it last. Not very hygienic at all!

I wasn't even five when I started school. I can still smell the polish on the school floor, buffed up and shiny, and the smell of the rubber plimsolls that we had to wear to help protect it. The strongest memory I have from my first day was hammering balls into a wooden block with holes in the top. We were each given a small slateboard and told to write our name or draw a picture in chalk, then bring it to the front for the teacher to see. The boy in front of me, funnily enough, was called George and he had been very tearful for most of the morning. When he handed over his slate board to the teacher it slipped from his hands and landed on the teacher's foot. We all held our breath as the teacher yelled out and performed a dance resembling the Highland fling. It was the first time I had seen George smile all day.

At a very young age I became aware of how cruel people could be towards each other. I could never quite understand the reasons for their bad behaviour, although I do remember when I developed a strong understanding of the meaning of the word 'feelings'.

My mother was a lone parent and when we moved from the countryside I was aware of only two adults in my life, my gran and my mother. If either my sister or I misbehaved my mother would threaten us with, 'I will put you both into a home for bad boys and girls and they will cut off your hair.' We both had long hair and we were very proud of it. Heaven only knows why it always looked so shiny – it must have been the big green bar of *Fairy* soap that we used because we hadn't enough money for shampoo. It was used for almost every household duty and always seemed to do the trick.

Money was scarce and so we relied on social benefits for support. Friends and neighbours were kind enough to give us second-hand clothes and my mother was very careful with the money she had. She would budget enough to take us on a short holiday to visit family in Edinburgh and England. However, there were many times when she had difficulty coping and if my sister and I were fighting this would often prove to be the icing on the cake. We would be sent packing, with all our worldly goods in a small suitcase, and escorted down the stairs into the street. Sometimes we would be told to sit on the step to the flat and wait for someone to take pity on us. The neighbours were kind enough to take us in until she calmed down, but when she got really stressed she would head for the river and threaten to jump off the Brig o' Balgownie and end it all.

One night when I was about nine years-old my mother stormed out saying she was never coming back. She did this quite often, but for some reason this time I felt sick. I found myself sweating, having trouble breathing and finding it hard to swallow. I remember the saliva running down my chin and my heart racing as feelings of terror crept in and the room span. Time seemed to stand still and the feeling seemed to go on forever. I felt like I was going to die. I got out of bed, shaking, and put on my clothes. I ran outside and down the street to my gran's new house, grateful she had recently moved nearer. I knocked hard on her door and woke her up. Frantically and out of breath I told her mum was going to jump into the river. Gran quickly calmed me down, smiled, then took my hand and sat me down. She told me not to worry, and that my mother had always been a drama queen when she got frustrated or didn't get her own way. She reassured me that it would have been nothing us girls had said or done and told me to get home before she got back, which gran assured me she would do once she had calmed down.

Just as my gran predicted my mother came back. Next morning at breakfast she just carried on as if nothing had happened the night before; she made our breakfast, cleaned our shoes ready for school and waved us off. I wanted to tell my teacher about my ordeal and why I was exhausted and unable to concentrate but it was difficult to catch her alone. She was always busy and I could hear my mother's voice clearly in my head saying, 'Children should be seen and not heard' and, 'What's said in these four walls will stay in these four walls.' So I decided to keep it to myself.

Mother's stressful episodes happened so frequently that I gradually began to wish she *would* jump in the river so we would not have to live in fear of the children's home. I was certain my sister and I did not do anything bad enough to make her so stressed out but off she would go again, and I would work myself up into a terrible state. All sorts of thoughts would go round my head and the home for bad children was always at the forefront of my mind.

The bad children's home that she nearly always threatened us with was an orphanage or refuge for children. The purpose-built facility was not far from where we lived and the children in the home were governed by a very strict set of rules. The children weren't allowed out after school, and most of my friends were told by their parents not to go near the home or they too would be in trouble. I clearly remember one parent saying, 'You don't know what they will do to you, so stay away.'

One day, while waiting in line for the teacher to open the classroom door, the girl standing in front of me was the new girl, who I knew lived in the children's home. I was curious to know why she was put into the home so I asked her. Almost immediately a voice from behind me said, 'Sandra, stop it! You'll hurt her feelings.' I felt my face go very hot and I was truly ashamed at myself for asking. My heart was racing again and I felt clammy. Something inside me knew it was wrong to ask, but I felt so threatened by my mother's behaviour that I needed to prepare myself for going to the home. I did apologise but there was a loud silence. Later that week I saw the girl from the home again but this time her beautiful long blond hair was cut short. I froze and had to fight back tears. I must have looked at her for some time as she came over and asked if I was all right. Again I apologised, and when I found my voice properly I asked about her hair.

I remember her reply as if it was yesterday: they all had to have short hair to protect everyone in the home from contracting head lice. Horrified, I couldn't take my eyes away from her face because she was smiling. She then told me, 'I have always wanted my hair short so don't look so sad.' She said that her father had always enjoyed a drink but when he lost his job his drinking had got worse, changing him from being a quiet, cheery man to being verbally aggressive. In a very short time his behaviour changed again as he become violent towards her mother. She told me her mother did not work and there was never much money brought in because her father drank most of it away. This always started an argument that escalated into violence. Her mother became so ill trying to protect herself and her two children that the doctor put her into a special hospital and the children went into the home. She told me that she was happy to be in the home because the people were kind and she felt safe, and that when her mother got well again they would all go back home.

Sadly I heard that her mother never did recover, though through all that pain I never heard her complain. She was attentive to her younger brother, taking on the role of mothering him. She was very mature for her young age. I was to hear in later years that her younger brother joined the Royal Navy and accidently drowned at sea.

I was inspired by her story and never again did I fear my

mother's threats of sending us to the home. It was clear to me that there were no bad children there, only troubled young people who were unfortunate to be born into troubled family relationships. I felt a huge weight had been lifted off of me. Years of worry melted away in those few minutes, just by talking and listening.

Another early experience of 'feelings' occurred when we were standing in line waiting to go into the dinner hall for our lunch. The children whose parents were on social benefits received free meals were told to stand at the back of the queue. If we skipped the queue we would be grabbed by the wrist and smartly walked to the back of the line as everyone sniggered and whispered about us. Not all teachers felt the same about this, but one older teacher would get her pleasure by refusing to let you pass until you said out loud for all to hear, 'I get free meals, Miss.' Quite a few would skip their meal when she was on dinner duty because they felt too ashamed to eat. I guess I was just too hungry to be bothered about feelings of shame, but I did feel angry at her attitude towards less fortunate children.

School was a struggle for me as I was never really the brightest. I seemed to lag behind most in my class in all the academic subjects. I would lose concentration very quickly because I could never seem to keep up. Some days I would go into class and spend most of my time daydreaming. I was exceptionally good at sport though, and this became my escape. I did not have the same fear as some of my friends when it came to challenges like the high jump or gymnastics. I loved to swim and would take pride diving in all sorts of twists off the highest boards at the local swimming pool. I also enjoyed being part of the synchronised swimming team.

Although I did struggle in class I always seemed to get a good report card that would comment on how hard I tried. I may never have been given the highest grades but the report showed I had tried my best. I felt good about that and so did my mother. However, there was usually a comment regarding my reading, saying my vocabulary was poor and it would likely improve if I took home my reading book and did the homework that was asked. I lied constantly about my homework and I loathed reading. When I opened a book the words would float around the pages and I felt sick to my stomach every time I had to read out loud.

One day in Religious Studies we all had to take turns reading a passage from the Bible. It would take me ages to work out what the words were, and the teacher got so frustrated he would make me the laughing stock of the class. He took great joy in encouraging the class to laugh at my struggles. He made me repeat the lines I got wrong and the names I could not pronounce, he smirked as he came up and stood beside me and put his figure on my Bible, pointing at each word, and he would mimic each word as I said it until I finished the paragraph. Before I knew what was happening to me the old feelings came back of sweaty hands, struggling to breathe and thinking I was going to die. I got so upset that day I ran out of the classroom to get away from everyone. Later, when I calmed down, I was punished with three rounds of the two-tongue leather strap across my hands, in front of the same classroom of children, as an example to anyone who dared to leave the room without permission. When the class had ended one of the boys came to me and said, 'Blimey, you're brave, was it not painful? You didn't flick an eye.' I then became the 'Brave One'. I would never again get emotional or show my pain to anyone. That day may have been the first time I got a whack from the leather belt but it was certainly not the last. I received many more as the years went past and I became the class scapegoat. I lost all respect for most of the teachers and I never held back what I felt. Life just seemed very unfair.

Many a time we would stand outside the music teacher's room waiting for her to open the door. There was a small window in the door through which you could see her standing, conducting a fantasy orchestra, stick in the right hand and the left hand going in circles at the wrist, eyes closed. She was lost in the moment, while we all stood outside taking turns to look through the window giggling, as you would expect at our age. During the music sessions, when the pupils played their own black plastic recorders with a white mouthpiece, I desperately wanted to join them. Mother couldn't afford a recorder so I asked for one for Christmas and was thrilled when I finally got one. It looked nothing like the others but I could play it very well. Turning up to class I took it out of its wooden box and joined in with the others, delighted to be playing with them at last. Unbeknown to me the recorder did not sound as sharp as the plastic ones and the teacher, who had a fine ear for sound, quickly picked me out. Again I was ridiculed and made to feel terrible. I was told never to bring that piece of wood back. I sat there for the remainder of the period feeling very disappointed, sad and frustrated.

The feeling of injustice didn't leave me until a long time later when I took part in the school concert. It was called *Rashiecoat* and was based on *Cinderella*. Somehow I had been given an important part on the xylophone; I was in charge of the clock chiming midnight. The look on the perfectionist music teacher's face when I banged, as hard as I could, thirteen strikes instead of twelve will remain in my mind forever. Her face spoke a thousand words as I looked straight into her eyes on the last bang. The xylophone bar almost jumped out of its socket from the sheer force with which I hit it.

When we got back to the class she looked down at me, shook her head in disgust and said, 'You used to be such a nice girl, I really don't know what's got into you.' I knew exactly what had got into me: it was her demeaning attitude. My actions did not hurt anyone else but it clearly upset her perfect performance.

Another time we were all asked to go on a school outing organised by the cooking teacher. The plan was to take the class to a shop in Aberdeen to see a new gadget operating – a liquidiser. I really was not interested in cooking and given that my mother had to stretch our income carefully I did not bother to ask her for the money. It was only when I told my teacher that I realised I'd made a terrible mistake. I explained we were not able to pay the money and it was okay because I wasn't that bothered about going on the trip. I expected that to be it and went to school as normal on the day of the trip. There were three of us altogether who did not go but instead of being given work to do we were sent to the music room to write one hundred lines. I couldn't understand why. We all came from low-income families and were being punished for it. We were told to write, 'I must make more of an effort to join the activities in class' one hundred times. I should have framed it.

At home things started to settle down at last. My mother met a man who would later become my stepfather and our lifestyle improved. We were no longer discriminated against for belonging to a single parent family living on social benefits.

We were now 'normal'. People stopped calling us 'tinks' and we were allowed to play with other children from upper-class areas without being judged. We owned a new car and would go out more socially, visiting new places. We became better off than others who used to look down on us; life was not such a struggle and mother's moods greatly improved.

Looking back now to the primary school days, it seems my brain was programmed by my teachers' discriminations, by friends and relatives' thoughts, beliefs and judgements. It was bombarded with other peoples' opinions, so much so that there was little room for my own thoughts to grow. I believe we lose our true self, the essence of who we could be, at a very early age.

I believed then that school was meant to encourage us all to grow and develop into mature young adults, providing us with the tools required to become part of society and help make a difference in the world. However, I found this difficult to accept given that our teachers displayed the most offensive attitude and behaviour!

I left school just scraping past, with no worthy grades but enough common sense to get me into work. My first job was with a wholesale company taking orders over the phone. However, this did not last long, as my spelling was so bad I'm sure everyone received the wrong order. I was the youngest there and everyone was kind but I knew it wasn't for me.

My friend worked with children in a hospital and suggested I should apply for a job there as they were recruiting auxiliary staff. This I did, and so began my long-lasting nursing carer.

Chapter 2

Back in the day

*"Life is like a game of snakes and ladders. You
will come across many snakes, but if you play
a fair game you will reach a healthier ending."*

My shift at the children's hospital started at 7 a.m., and although I had made a brief visit to some of the wards before I
took up the post, I was not really prepared for my first day. I had
not expected to see so many little souls with so many deformi-
ties – some with their joints and limbs contracted and unable
to move, almost every child needing help to dress, feed and
wash, every one of them wearing nappies. Daily physiotherapy
was needed to keep mucus from filling their tiny lungs. I spent
my first morning terrified that I would hurt them when trying
to dress them, and afraid I might choke them when feeding
them with liquidised food. Most of all I found it very difficult
to interact with the small, helpless little children. The next
day while I was standing at the bus stop I remember having a
panic attack. I felt my pulse race, my mouth went dry, and my
heart beat faster. As the bus appeared my palms became sweaty
and my stomach churned – I had been traumatised by my first
day. I just couldn't face another day with those poor, helpless

little souls. I was afraid I would cause them pain and further suffering, so I turned and ran home.

I have my stepfather to thank for what happened next. He put me in the car and took me straight back to the children's hospital; as I was late for my shift he explained my anxieties to the staff. It did take me a long time to settle in to this type of nursing, but it didn't take me long to see past all the twisted limbs and restricted joints. The children had a lot to offer and if you managed to get a smile it was a great feeling of connection. You knew they were quite content in their own wee world, which started to not seem quite so painful after all. I look back now and believe that it was my own pain I was feeling at the beginning. I was only seventeen years old and wasn't confident enough in myself. I didn't have the necessary knowledge or understanding of their unique disabilities and needs. It was a very specialised area of nursing and I now treasure those experiences, recognising them as a rewarding beginning to my career.

I worked with the children for a few years then left when I was encouraged to enroll for nurse training. That was in 1976. I trained for two years at Foresterhill Nursing College, which was attached to the Aberdeen Royal Infirmary. The building is no longer there today.

At the nursing college we were taught to treat people with the kindness with which you would expect to be treated yourself. I strongly believed that those words were at the core of peoples' recovery.

The wards were tidy, the floors were buffed daily (you could almost eat off them), the windows were always opened to let fresh air circulate, and the beds were tidy, with the famous hospital corners keeping things orderly. There was a strict regime to be followed in most wards: we were expected to memorise every patient's name and their condition before the doctor's round, everyone received a well balanced diet, and fresh water was available to patients on top of their locker. Pressure area care involved massage and turning a patient's position in bed every two hours, particularly for immobile patients who found it hard to turn over by themselves. Strict bed rest was imposed and there was silence for a cat-nap after lunch. Visitors were restricted to two at a time and putting the ward lights out at 10 p.m. was a top priority, as rest was vital to recovery.

The system of matrons, sisters, staff nurses (pinkies), enrolled nurses, auxiliaries, and domestic staff made for a good team structure. Everyone was valued, everyone had a job to do, and everyone knew what their responsibilities were. We all demonstrated respect for each other and took pride in our appearance, with our starched uniforms, hats, and soft-soled white shoes.

Domestic staff were a highly valued part of the nursing team. They communicated with patients regularly, making sure they had plenty of clean water, and they would often notice small changes in patients that the busy nurses missed. The domestic staff knew who was not eating their meals or taking their medication and would inform us. Some patients would confide in them with their worries or fears, and the domestic staff knew when to pass information on to us if they felt that it was important to a patient's recovery. The wards were kept clean, morale was good and patients felt safe.

Patients were encouraged to take time to rest and heal their bodies; some were later transported to convalescing homes to fully recover before being sent home. Of course mistakes did occur, but staff were honest enough to stand up and take responsibility, improving by reflecting, evaluating, sharing and applying this to strengthening future care. There was not much need for the amount of documentation that we have today, as all the vital recordings were simple to record and patients shared the responsibility of doing what they could to help themselves.

I nursed in various areas, including those of maternity, mental health, and vulnerable children. I then moved out of the hospital setting to become a community nurse, working for the out-of-hours evening and all-night care services. This fitted in well with my lifestyle, and I was fortunate to go to work in the evenings when my children were tucked up in bed. Community nursing involved supporting families in their own homes while loved ones faced the end stages of their life.

For my final twelve years I worked in the care of the elderly. This was my forte; I loved working with our elderly population. It was extremely interesting and rewarding to listen to their stories, to hear how they struggled to survive with very little through two terrifying wars. I also gained tremendous knowledge in human behaviour and family dynamics over the years by supporting not only the senior citizens but also their extended families. Towards the end of my career I was involved in childhood immunisations and supported the clinical nursing staff when they were busy.

However, times have changed and sadly so did the 75+ health screening (informally called the MOT). This service was extremely valued by both GPs and the public. It provided anticipatory care to everyone over the age of 75, assessing any mental, physical and social difficulties while liaising with other services to prevent major health problems developing.

This service ended due to lack of money and planned changes to the way nursing care in future was to be delivered. It is only now that we are beginning to feel the loss of this valuable service as the NHS is faced with blocked beds, and the public with feelings of isolation.

The re-design has changed the way nursing care is to be delivered. We now have practice-attached nurses who are responsible for referring patients to delivery teams. These patients will be registered at their chosen practice. If treatment is required and patients are unable to get to the surgery, the direct community delivery care team will then provide care in the patient's home catchment area.

However, before I manage to publish this book I'm sure the re-design will be altered by some other re-design as demands escalate. My duty mainly involved sending through referrals, which involved lots of paperwork and computer technology. I desperately missed the hands-on approach and began to feel very demotivated. I needed a change so started looking around at my options, although I found it very difficult to leave my comfort zone. I loved my job as a nurse, I loved the people whom I worked with and I loved giving a service to elderly people. I also loved being part of a well-organised nursing team and helping our tired GPs at the Hamilton Medical Group, whose role has also changed dramatically over time.

Chapter 3

Prison nursing

"We are all perfect because we are individuals given different challenges to conquer."

When I told my work colleagues I was moving on and going to work in Aberdeen prison, the most common response was, 'Why on earth would you want to go and work in a prison?'

The final straw came during an in-service study day that aimed to make us aware of the latest 'do's and dont's' of a delicate procedure. There was to be an exam at the end of it. If we got less than eighty per cent correct we would get no certificate.

Well, on the word 'exam' my brain went into spasm. I am dyslexic and had not sat an exam since secondary school. I thought there was no way I would ever remember what a number seven bowel motion looked like, let alone describe it in a written exam, so in a fight to survive the day I took the trainer aside and explained the difficulties that I had with my recall memory, especially when under direct pressure.

Sadly this confession led to nothing as I was reduced to tears of anger and frustration after failing the exam with only seventy per cent. However, I was offered an appointment to go over the questions I had failed.

Seventy per cent was good enough for me, I thought, and I can imagine anyone who has struggled with dyslexia would agree. The thought of resitting the exam filled me with dread, and I had been increasingly unsettled with the new direction my job was taking me in anyway, so I decided that enough was enough. After forty years NHS Grampian had finally driven me behind bars.

The NHS became responsible for health care in Scottish prisons at the end of 2011. Joining the Scottish prison service and the NHS has been one of the biggest challenges the NHS has faced this century, and a shortage of experienced staff was causing an extremely limited service to Aberdeen Craiginches Prison, resulting in some community nurses being asked to put their name forward to cover staff shortages.

I jumped at the opportunity of this new challenge and as it was only for a few days a week I felt I could cope with the change. So I approached our manager I asked if I could be seconded to the prison services.

I was led to believe that a normal day at the prison would consist of medicating, wound care, and the organising and running of clinics. With my past experience in mental health I thought I would get a lot of good experience out of the post.

A short history of the prison

Craiginches Prison was completed in 1891 by D. Andrew and Co for £19,000. According to an extract published by the *Aberdeen Journal* on 10 June 1891, forty-three prisoners were initially transported to Craginches from the old county jail. Craiginches Prison also held Henry John Burnett, the last man to be hanged in Scotland.

Henry John Burnett was convicted of shooting his lover's husband, Mr Thomas Guyan, and sentenced to death at the High Court in Aberdeen on 25 July 1963. A crowd of protesters gathered outside the prison as they believed Henry, known as Harry, did not receive a fair trial due to his mental health issues. The trial lasted two days and at the age of twenty-one he was executed.

Craiginches was a medium-security prison; however, there was still a great deal of supervision and security to prevent prisoners from escaping. It was originally designed to house 155 prisoners but was recorded at one point to have held 264; it was known as one of the most overcrowded prisons in Scotland. Men made up the majority of the prison population, but there was a block that held a few women who were near the end of their sentence and required support to adapt back into society.

The clink

Have you ever wondered why it is called the clink?

If you enter a prison for the first time either working, visiting, or being imprisoned then you will have your own experience of it. For me, as I walked up the few steps which lead to the entrance, I remember facing a very large steel door with a peculiar, cold, T-shaped door handle which moved left and right with a clinking sound.

If you were a nurse or officer you had to identify yourself

with picture ID, then collect a thick black belt that clipped tightly round your waist. It supported your alarm, two-way radio, a bunch of keys, and anything else you could clip on if you dared. Whatever extras you attached to your waist would need a risk assessment, as I found out the hard way.

There were only a certain number of items you could strap around your waist and still be able to run up the three flights of stairs to the top floors, which you might have to suddenly do at the piercing sound of your vibrating waist alarm. Of course this is bearing in mind that you also had to carry the required oxygen cylinder and large bag full of other lifesaving equipment. It wasn't only the stairs you had to contend with though – you would also have to fight your way through never-ending heavy metal gates, desperately trying to work out which key to use as you struggled to hold things together, with the cables of the two-way radio and ear-piece flapping around waiting to get caught on the edge of something and rip your ear off, all the while with the continuous radio chatter going on in your brain from officers speaking in a language surely only known to aliens.

Welcome to prison nursing – a truly challenging experience!

Day one

From the very first day it was evident that this nursing was radically different to anything I had experienced in my forty years with the health board.

When I arrived the team was short-staffed and, with very little understanding of the expectations they had of me, I was stunned. I stood there feeling helpless and in the way.

People were buzzing around everywhere like bees who would sting you if you got in their way. They were only focused on the task at hand, the job that had to be done before alarms would sound and the prison faced a lockdown. During a lockdown there would be no movement in the prison until the situation was resolved, so they felt that they had to get their jobs done quickly.

I remember standing in the middle of that hive wondering how on earth I had got there and feeling totally out of my depth. I was a community nurse, for goodness sake! I had loved my job with the Hamilton Medical Group: was this chaos really worth giving up the tedious paperwork for? I hoped that at any moment I would wake up and the nightmare would be over. Just then though I felt a tug at my sleeve that brought me back to the moment, and a kind, gentle voice asked, 'Are you okay?' It was the charge nurse, who constantly reassured me that things would get better, that everyone felt like this when they came to prison for the first time. I began to wonder at what side of the bars I was on.

When I took up post NHS and SPS staff were mostly leaving to find new jobs as the prison was due to close. Many did not wish to uproot their families to the new prison forty miles away. During this time unfamiliar nursing staff and Scottish prison staff came from all parts of Grampian and elsewhere to support the already stretched service. For almost a year everyone covered each other's shifts to support things but it soon became evident that we were struggling to cope even with basic care. Tempers got out of control and we were behaving worse than children in a school playground; staff were stressed and burning out, nurses went off sick and some even resigned. It was also a very difficult time for the patients in custody.

Some had complex needs and we were struggling to provide the quality care they desperately needed.

No matter how hard the managers tried to get staff cover, things still did not improve and we were exhausted. Mistakes were made, which resulted in stricter controls and more time-consuming exercises, which in turn added more pressure and more mistakes. There seemed to be no end to the toxic energy floating around us. I'm sure most of the nurses went home in tears after their shift. I know I did at least once a week, if not more often.

In our endless struggles we did ask our managers for help, so a meeting was arranged featuring various health associates, union representatives, management, pharmacists, human resources and prison security officers. I'm going to be honest and admit that the meeting was about as useful as a wet paper bag.

One health and safety issue was brought to the attention of the management though and is worth a mention. It was a routine nursing task to medicate patients in the halls twice daily. We were expected to carry a toolbox full of drugs in one hand and a carrier bag with three A4 folders containing more than eighty prescription sheets, as well as a jug for water and plastic cups, in the other hand, then open four heavy steel doors to gain access to the halls, then lock each door behind us as we went through. It would have been easy for one of us to be taken hostage, as the medication had a monetary value in prison. We highlighted this with all who attended the meeting.

The union rep was very helpful with his advice: he thought the answer was for the nurse and health care worker to come up with an idea that we would all agree upon.

Many ideas were put forward but as usual no one agreed. Although the prison security showed great interest and provided support that soon fell through due to staffing issues, and we all went back to the way things were before. Finally a temporary member of the nursing staff took time on her day off to buy another tool box smaller than the one in use. It was clearly not big enough for the quantity of medication required to be issued, and she also completely forgot to buy a lock, which was the whole point of the exercise. However, it was in her own time and at least she made the effort. Nowadays more and more nurses would agree that they have endless responsibilities and expectations put upon them.

The challenges in a prison are as complex as in any other community setting, but there seemed to be a lack of understanding from other services when it came to custodial health care. Staff caring for a patient in custody struggle to keep appointments due to the strict prison regime and security responsibilities that need to be in place. The time spent with each patient can also be compromised as nursing staff have to uphold and respect prison boundaries.

When you have two services working alongside each other it can cause a great deal of pressure. It can be difficult for all involved to maintain a safe working environment, especially when relying on agency or bank nurses from community and hospital settings. These nurses have very little specialist training on the effects of drug and alcohol misuse before joining the team, which added an extra burden on the already exhausted prison staff. I witnessed first-hand the effect this had on the patients in custody as they were denied services that we were expected to provide but were unable to.

Staff morale was at its lowest when I joined the prison,

and as the prison was preparing to close its doors for good the working environment became increasingly toxic. Staff and prisoners were unsure where they were being moved to, causing anxieties and tension to rise. It was almost Christmas and groups of prisoners were preparing to be moved to other Scottish prisons for a few months, allowing time for the new prison at Peterhead to be completed. It was stressful for all involved as we tried to maintain a service and were expected to pack up equipment with no extra staff.

At times the service almost ground to a halt as we were dependent on bank nurses who were confined to the clinic area (they did not have the right SPS training required to enter the halls). Often only one nurse would be on duty to medicate almost sixty patients and to receive and assess the health of new prisoners from court. There could be as many as eight new prisoners in any one evening, and processing could take anything up to thirty minutes per patient. Many required an interpreter, which also took up valuable time. We had to organise the paperwork for transfers the following day, as well as attend to diabetics and asthma sufferers to ensure their safety through the night. Unlike hospital wards where you could stay behind and complete tasks if necessary, the prison had a policy of locking their doors before a certain time, meaning all keys, alarms, and radios had to be handed in and accounted for before anyone was allowed to leave the premises at night.

Patient clinics were stopped, important health checks cancelled; near the end we were both grateful for and dependent on the kindness of the nurses from Peterhead prison, who travelled forty miles to support us.

Chapter 4

Patients behind bars

*"You are not your behaviour, your behaviour
is just a symptom of the challenges you have
faced."*

Most of us are guilty of judging people by our own moral standards and experiences, but the truth is that any one of us could find ourselves behind bars; it can take less than a second to lose concentration and cause an accident, to change our path and the paths of our loved ones forever.

We are all unique and are all responsible for dealing with our own life's traumas and dramas. We do this in the only way we can: with the knowledge and understanding we have developed as we grow up and live in society, depending on the support and understanding of family, friends and community resources. However, for many people life's path seems set out from the day they were born. Many do not have anyone they feel they can trust.

Some people show no morals and place no value in themselves or others; some may have been medically proven to be psychopaths and need to be locked away to protect our communities. To this group we are nothing more than objects; we seem to simply be a thing with no human value. One man I spoke to said he was repulsed by his own actions and hated himself, then stated he has no control,: 'It's the way I'm wired and that's that.' The future for many like him will be limited by bars, as science may never be able to find a solution to help us reach them. If such a person has traumatised you please seek help, and try to understand that their actions were all about them and nothing about you.

The Oxford dictionary states that a prisoner is, 'A person legally committed to prison as a punishment for a crime or while waiting trial'. However, I have heard prisoners being described with words like 'scum', 'delinquents', 'lunatics' and more. This is not who they are, it is only how they are perceived. One milder name I have heard being used is 'weeds'. To me, weeds are colourful flowers in the wrong place. If put in the correct place they may blend in, flourish, and grow.

Prison is a point of correction; being sent to prison is a sentence that the judge decides fits the evidence of the crime, with the intention of keeping the public and prisoner safe from further harm. It is a myth that people are sent to prison to be punished, although of course in the strictest sense prison certainly is a punishment. The punishment doesn't stop with prison either. Depending on the crime some people will never walk entirely free – they might not be accepted into other countries because of their criminal record, even if they have truly changed their ways. Someone who has been through the correction procedure may never be able to work or holiday abroad. Some sentences continue for a lifetime outwith prison.

While the strict regime and loss of freedom is indeed a punishment, the real purpose of imprisonment is to allow time to think, to allow time for an inmate to consider how they can turn their lives around. It gives time for someone to look back on their lives and wonder how they got there in the first place, time to rehabilitate, time for another chance, time to be forgiven by others, and time to pray for forgiveness from the people whose lives they have perhaps destroyed. They are in prison care with the hope that they may be corrected, educated, reformed; it may be the only chance they have in their already chaotic lives to learn about the morals that are acceptable in today's society.

Prison is a place for people to be given the chance to be reborn. For many who are sent to prison, a crime may have been inflicted on them first, perhaps at a young and important time in their lives. Many prisoners that I spoke to confessed they were subjected to abuse from the people who were supposed care for them, people they felt they could trust.

In fact, the majority of men in prison have suffered some degree of emotional trauma in their childhood. This could be abandonment, rejection, or perhaps they have been in and out of foster care or various childcare homes. Many men have gone through their early years within chaotic families. Such a start in life can cause deep-seated emotional pain, which is often hidden by the use of alcohol and drugs. Although many can still find it in their hearts to forgive their abusers, their subconscious emotions may cause them to act out unconsciously in ways they themselves, not to mention others close to them, don't understand. Anger is a deep-seated sadness which is emotionally painful.

On admission to prison from court prisoners would be seen by a nurse to assess their general health and wellbeing. I often found this to be the most valuable time I spent with these men, as here confessions of shame and guilt were common.

They were shocked and ashamed by what they had heard about themselves in the court; many would break down and cry. I eventually became aware of similarities between people in their initial behaviour and attitude during their assessment. The new prisoners regularly betrayed a very sensitive, child-like nature, some discussed the history of their traumas, most showed evidence of being extremely emotionally bright.

I commonly came across people with strong memories of being a rebel in their past, people who had never been able to shake off their frustration and who found it hard to control anger that built up inside them. Most were easily annoyed and quick to react. They would find themselves fighting in situations that were nothing to do with them, feeling they could not stand back and watch their friends who were unable to defend themselves being bullied, or they got upset when they saw people who they felt were hard done by. They could be set off by the sheer unfairness of anything, particularly relationships.

Others felt they could not find anywhere that they fitted in. In prison they became confused and disorientated, struggling when they were expected to adapt to systems and take orders that they simply did not understand. They were used to living in chaotic situations and so were unable to relax from their constant state of hyperawareness, also finding it hard to sleep.

These stories led me to believe that most prisoners did not have good fortune from a very young age; the core basic needs of love, shelter and food had never been met so they had trouble fitting into society and struggled to survive in the complicated world they found themselves in. Some confessed that they felt like they didn't belong to anyone and felt very vulnerable, isolated and confused. Sadly for many, prison is all they know. I've often had people tell me that they get so frightened and exhausted they deliberately commit crimes so they can get locked up. Believe me, Craiginches was no place you would call home, no matter what the media think. The men were confined, often in twos, to cubicles just big enough to hold a bunk bed and table. Most share a confined room with a stranger for the best part of twenty-four hours a day for years.

That said, I'm not about to make excuses for these troubled men as we all have choices in life. If we make mistakes we can either learn from them and move on, or stick and be stuck. We all have our own personal views and if a criminal has affected you then you may feel they deserve what they get. But I would urge people not to brand everyone by the same book. Some of our pensioners are in prison because they cannot pay their debts, and not all prisoners are evil beings.

Many men whom I assessed were victims of behaviour learned from the families they were born into, and many crimes are committed because of the need to fulfil habits – some from the need of addictive substances, some from 'the adrenaline rush' or to 'dampen emotional pain'. But the majority of criminals are crying out for our help and would do anything to feel that they belonged, had a purpose, and fitted in somewhere in our society.

I remember a conversation I had one evening with the prison chaplain after he had finished his routine visit. He said, 'These men have stopped growing, they all seem to be stuck just like children, the way they speak and act.' I agreed – many of our prisoners were physically grown men with the mind of a child. They had somehow stopped maturing, perhaps due to childhood trauma, perhaps through missing out on some key stage of personal development or growth, perhaps through all the missed weeks of school. They were frightened children trapped inside an adult's body, still mentally stuck at the age the in which their trauma started.

Our society does tend to blame parents for children's troubled lives, but in my experience prisoners most often spoke about being bullied as far back as school either by friends or teachers, some by members of their extended family. Many such victims of bullying only realised they had been bullied once the definition was explained to them. They were surprised to find that they themselves had also been bullying others, and were not aware of the emotional damage that they had inflicted on people's mental and physical health.

Men of all ages told a similar story of how they began dealing drugs, saying that they did not want their families suffer the poverty they were brought up with. They felt guilty that their parents had to work so hard, sometimes in two or three different jobs at once, just to put food on the table and a roof over their heads. They could not see the damage they were doing by selling drugs, with one person memorably telling me that there would always be a market for drugs because people would always want them. He argued that everyone had a choice of whether to take drugs or not, and it was easy money which his family benefited from.

Tom's story

Now I realise what I have done. I lie in my cell, cut off from my family for the next seven years. My daughter and son will be seven years older when I get out; seven Christmases missed, seven family holidays, seven school parents' night. The worst day of my life is when I got the call that my father died and I was standing at his grave handcuffed. Not only did I bring shame to my family, but I let myself down all for the sake of material things, things that now don't seem as important. Money means nothing when you lose your family but at the time you just don't see further than the immediate result, not thinking of the consequences of who you sell to and the cost of seven years of my life. I'm just lucky no one died from my actions.

I asked how being in prison had changed his thinking, and he said:

Time goes by so slowly, the days are long and the nights longer. You have time to think more about your life and I tend to go deeper. I used to hear voices in my head continually chatting, reminding me of my worthlessness; I became paranoid. I know this can be a result of drug abuse but on the outside I would reach out for more drugs to escape the voices, but in here there is no escape; you have to deal with the demons.

Ed's Story
I used to steal cars for the thrill of a joy run, I would sometimes return the cars back to where I stole them almost empty of petrol. I'm not sure why I did it. At home I came from a large family, there were five of us. However, we were all different natured and my father would always spoil my younger brother. He was the baby of the family and I was the second oldest. My father favoured my younger brother and he just could not see the rest of us. I remember once he asked me to fix the garden fence and I did; he gave me money when I had finished and I thanked him, then later when we

were in company he would say things like the fence was not straight and I had the cheek to take money off him. No matter what I did it was never right, he was never pleased. My younger brother died in a tragic accident and fifteen years later he still grieves the loss and sees the rest of us as falling short. The rest of us just don't seem to exist in his eyes and it really hurts.

Dick's Story

I confessed I had jumped a red light, collided with another car, which had fatal consequences. Being in prison is nothing compared to the guilt I will carry now for the rest of my life. I understand and accept the anger of relatives of the person involved in the accident, how many 'if only's' do you hear people say. All I want to do now is turn back the clock but I can't – I have destroyed someone's family and my own. The only thing that I can offer now is to tell people to slow down and pay attention as one wrong move, one split second and lapse of concentration can change your whole life. It took less than a second to end a life and change other lives for ever. I feel sad, very sad and sorry for being the cause of so much loss and grief. It really doesn't matter if people find it in their hearts to forgive me as I can't see any way to ever forgive myself. It wasn't that I was speeding, or drunk, I was just not paying attention. For some reason I lost concentration, daydreaming perhaps, and all it took was that split second.

The conversation that sticks with me the most is the story of a father who lost control when some teenagers tormented his daughter. His young daughter was playing on her bike in her garden when a few youths decided to join her; she was very frightened and ran inside to tell her father.

Harry's Story

I confronted the lads and they just laughed at me. After I received some spitting and verbal abuse they went away, but they returned later that day and shouted abuse through my letterbox, threatening to sexually assault my daughter some day when she walked home from school. Then after they'd taken turns on her bike they ran off. I went after the teenagers and caught up with one as the others got away, in a split second, with feelings of raging anger over the threats made to my daughter, the youth that I caught took the angry punches for all three of them. He needed hospital treatment after he fell on the ground, banging the back of his head. He said in court I had kicked him in the head and to tell the truth I really do not remember, I was in such an angry state I believe I was capable of anything.

The father was later sent to prison for assault and no charge was made against the other youths for their threatening behaviour. It was not a planned attack – he was provoked and did not think of the consequences at the time. He was in a blind rage and when he came to himself he was shocked to see what he had done.

It makes you consider how far you would go to protect your own child, given that we are all from the animal world. Has it not been proved by scientists that a basic human instinct is the 'fight or flight'? Have you ever seen how seagulls attack humans if they dare walk near their young?

I remember an incident involving my own baby, which took place at the community playgroup. I had a child almost two years old and a baby a few weeks old. There was no room in the play area for my pram so I left my baby in the dining room across from the play area. I heard crying sounds from the dining room and when I went through I found a small child standing on the front wheel of my pram punching and scratching my baby's face. I got such a shock, and as I picked the child up off the wheel of the pram I froze. I remember turning round and putting the child down, but I was so traumatised I could not pick up my own child who at this time had blood all over his tiny face. When I look back at that incident it would have been so easy to have reacted differently. It would have been human instinct to defend my baby and pull the child off the pram, and I could easily have thrown the child to the back of the room. I dread to think what would have happened had I not frozen – I too could have been behind bars thanks to my natural human instinct to protect my young.

However, it must be said that there were others in prison who could quite easily receive a Nobel Prize for manipulation, if there ever was such a prize. They could lie to themselves so accurately they would have the Pope believe them. There is an old saying that you cannot tell the same lie twice, but some prisoners were so good at believing their own lies they could do it accurately many times over.

Some young men may not have been encouraged to express themselves or been allowed the opportunity to grow by overprotective parents, or by parents who found themselves in unstable relationships. One man explained to me that although he loved both his parents dearly he felt like a prisoner in his own home because of their inability to let him wander far from sight. This was due to their own fears and beliefs, to their view of the world as a very dangerous place. Another man stated at times he felt very vulnerable and out of control when engaging in relationships, saying, 'I felt overwhelmed after a few dates. I found women were very demanding and when getting intimate I thought was going to die.' He then went on to explain that his father was a quiet man with nothing much to say for himself. However, his mother made up for this by never stopping speaking, even if it was about nothing of relevance. He said she used to shout at his father a lot because he just ignored her and it could be quite scary: 'She was as big as her voice.'

He went on to explain that his parents didn't have much in common and that, looking back, he was frustrated at his dad for not standing up to his mother and for accepting her strict routine just to keep the peace. It was so hard to please her that he would often become frustrated with both his parents. He believed now that he had adopted a reflection of his mother's behaviour, which had a lot to do with his physical and emotional outbursts at the time when he went off the rails. He then went on to say:

Eventually when I took my freedom, I found women would quickly fall for me for some reason and set demands. I started resenting women I got involved with and would try to control them. I was able to manipulate them to get my own way and eventually got really abusive if I was denied this. It became a game – I wasn't really looking for a long-term relationship at the time but would never be the one to break up. I believe I was acting out my anger. I did not like who I had become; I felt disgusted with myself most of the time but most of all I was annoyed at women who would love me regardless of the abuse I gave them. Most women thought they were capable of fixing me, but at that time I believed there was nothing wrong with me. Nevertheless I did not like myself very much and somehow needed to prove I was worthless and not worthy of love. I guess I did not really understand relationships much, and never really knew what I was looking for. Now look at me! Instead of my mother's strict routine it's a prison regime, and that gets me down more than anything, but I guess I did need fixing after all.

One of the younger prisoners asked me one day if there was anyone available to help him with anger management therapy, as he knew he needed to control his anger. Unfortunately at that time there was no one available to refer him to. I asked if he could explain a bit about what set off the feelings of anger, and he told me that as a child he had always tried his best to please his family but he came from a family of perfectionists. His mother had an obsessive nature and his father was a workaholic:

I often bought my mum presents to cheer her up. I felt she was lonely when my dad was away; however, it was either the wrong colour or the wrong size, nothing was ever appreciated and not even the thought counted. She would always tell me how to dress, how to style my hair. I loved her but never felt good about myself or good enough for her. Once I bought her flowers and a blue vase for Mother's Day and put it on the kitchen table so she could see it in the morning when she got up. When I came home she asked me to take the vase back to the shop for a red one as it did not match the kitchen. Trivial this may sound as an example but I was very sad and upset and embarrassed to have returned it and I broke down tears in the shop; then I would get angry at myself later and short-tempered about small issues that trigger a rage in me. That's why I am in here, I can't control my temper.

From my short time in the prison I was able to identify three common types of trauma that people suffer from when they are young:

The child who feels abandoned

This child has been left in some way. It may have been through some tragic circumstances like the death of their parents or guardian, divorce or adoption. They might come from a large family whose parents haven't been able to spend enough time with each child individually. They may feel abandoned because their parents were too busy working and they were left to provide for themselves. Or perhaps a mother has re-married and the child is no longer her only focus. This can result in someone fearing that they will be abandoned again. They can be very lonely, desperate for attention, and continually seek reassurance that they are safe and wanted.

The neglected child

This child would have been left alone without much food, warm clothes, or love. They would have been pushed to the side by their parents and never made to feel like they had any value or purpose, meaning they believe that they are not lovable or worthwhile. They are depressed and want to to hide and cry. This neglect results in their finding it difficult to express feelings in words; later in life they may not be able to demonstrate love or know how to love.

The spoiled child

This child wants what they don't need, and they want it now. If they don't get it they'll throw a temper tantrum and in the end their demands will be met (watch the movie *Charlie and the Chocolate Factory* and spot the one!). This carries over into adulthood with disastrous effects.

Back in the fifties the first relationship you had was with your mother as most women were expected to stay at home, bring up the children and take care of the house. Fathers were rarely about; many worked away from home or for long hours.

When I was a child my mother just had to look at me in a certain way to completely destroy my day. As I grew older and stronger her looks did not bother me in the same way because I had learned to look away, but she then turned to words, which were worse. They would penetrate my stomach, causing extreme cramping, then surface and repeat themselves whenever someone triggered a memory of something she had said.

The power of the words she used against me could have crippled me for a lifetime, but fortunately my experience over her children's home threat saved me. I no longer trusted what she said and chose to walk away from her negative attitude and behaviour. I could dedicate a whole chapter to mother and child relationships, but that's not really the purpose of this book (and a chapter probably wouldn't be long enough anyway!). I would heartily recommend the book *When you and your mother can't be friends* by Victoria Secunda. It's a must-read for those looking for support and understanding when struggling with their relationship with their mother.

As a child you tend to keep negative feelings to yourself, storing them in the chemistry of your body and the wiring of your brain. Thoughts, feelings and emotions can be stored like this for years, festering away, unnoticed until one day an old memory gets triggered. Perhaps it's some music you have heard, or a familiar smell. Our memory can surprise us at any given time. Once these unpleasant feelings are triggered they can come rushing back. You might even begin to feel sick, or you can't sleep, and you begin to struggle to regain control of your thoughts.

Negative childhood feelings can show up later in life and result in an adult searching for a comfort, something to help relax or to provide them with the necessary courage to carry on. It's very easy for this to get out of control, with people buying things they can't afford, dabbling in drugs or gambling just to get a surge of happiness. This then leads to a further downward spiral: getting into debt, dealing drugs, becoming ashamed of themselves.

Bottling up pain, over time, results in both mind and body breaking down, causing a change in attitude, behaviour and character. It's like a simmering volcano, the boiling hot lava churning up inside, waiting for something to trigger a painful memory. Soon the volcano turns into one big explosion as aggression and abuse spews out in all directions, hurting whatever it comes in contact with.

Many people go to great lengths to try to get back what they feel they have lost. In doing so they become self-absorbed – everything becomes an object getting in the way of their need to survive. They lose their dignity and reasoning, they blame others to make themselves feel better because they don't want to believe they have stooped so low. Some get buried so deep in their trouble that they become afraid and paranoid, and they look for other ways to feel alive or release the pressure – perhaps by self-harming, or in extreme circumstances by taking their own life.

It is common for prisoners not to have registered with a GP, which may be why there are so many undiagnosed mental health issues. Sometimes behaviour related to mental health issues can be looked upon as normal due to someone's social upbringing, resulting in a delayed medical diagnosis and delayed treatment. I found it very difficult to meet a prisoner's individual needs when I had little medical history to go on. A lack of medical history may also be detrimental to the sentence some prisoners have been given at the time of judgment in court.

Many patients behind bars suffer from various forms of mental illness, such as schizophrenia, which is a disturbance of perception and thoughts. This clearly has an effect on their actions outside as well as inside prison. These patients would often tell me of hallucinations or delusions they were experiencing, as well as their struggle with paranoia and depression. They often said they withdrew from members of their family and general society as they simply could not cope. Their families could not understand as they found it hard to put into words how they felt.

Alcohol and unprescribed drugs sadly only make psychotic symptoms worse, and self-medicating reduces compliance with a prescribed course of medication. Depression in prison was also evident, with some showing symptoms such as self-blame, disturbed sleep, tiredness, guilt, sadness, and recurring suicidal thoughts. Often we would see two types of depression – one related to the guilt of the crime they committed, the other that had begun before they committed their crime (which could have occurred as an indirect result of their depression). Personality and social anxiety disorders were also common. These conditions are treatable if diagnosed early, and early treatment might well have prevented many of those men from committing a criminal offence.

I was amazed to find that many patients in custody were extremely talented and often able to express themselves through art and poetry. I quite quickly realised how pleasant and polite most were when speaking to them alone, not just because of the threat of the strict behaviour policies, but because they felt they were in a safe environment. Of course, some could act up, but I found most to have good manners and strong moral beliefs. They generally accepted their lot, though they would have their moans just like everyone else. Most seemed to look out for each other and would confide in each other. The majority seemed to be able to connect on a deeper emotional level. Being male they did go to great lengths to hide their emotions, but when alone you could see in their eyes the pain and torment they so desperately tried to hide. Perhaps if people had more knowledge of how the brain works then those men may have had a better understanding of how they got to where they were.

'Craigie', as the prison was known, finally closed its doors at the beginning of 2014. The prisoners were moved to the new Grampian prison, a state-of-the-art building in Peterhead. It was not before time. Some may question why so much money was spent on a prison, and some may believe that criminals don't deserve such comforts. Such views may look justified when, soon after opening, a complete unit of the prison was destroyed by forty men at a cost to the tax payer of £246,000. However, if we look at prison as a place for reform rather than a place purely for punishment then things are not quite so clear.

To those who are keen to work as a nurse in a prison I would say that you definitely need to be good at forward thinking and to not be afraid of being challenged. It is a unique and rewarding nursing experience, but there is a great deal to learn. Another thing I cannot stress enough is the importance of paying close attention to your confidentially responsibilities, as endorsed by the Nursing & Midwifery Council (NMC) professional code of conduct. You may want to have a copy of this document next to your bed as it is crucial you have a good understanding of its contents. The NMC code of professional conduct 2002 states that:

Each nurse shall act at all times in such a manner as to safeguard and promote the interests of individual patients and clients; serve the interests of society; justify public trust and confidence, and uphold and enhance the good standing and reputation of the profession.

Good advice indeed!

The diversity of the prison service is unique; it is a specialised area of practice which requires early recognition of health and social needs to prevent further ill health. Nurses must be able to assess and then maintain the best treatment within an extremely challenging setting. Often situations do arise that are out of the nurse's control, situations that inevitably compromise the nurse's ability to provide spontaneous, direct care. It can be frustrating for nurses to accept some of the strict restrictions that apply to the mentally ill patients

I believe we can all do a little bit more. Sometimes all it takes to change how someone feels is understanding and taking the time to listen properly. This may be all you need to do to make a huge difference in someone's life, lessen the financial cost to society, and to improve the health and wellbeing of us all.

Chapter 5

Costs and relationships

"We all need money to help the external world go round, but we all need love and gratitude to make our internal world healthy."

Although the NHS is still one of the best health services in the world, the truth is that the NHS piggy bank is cracked. There is not enough in the pot to save it from breaking into a million pieces. The NHS is now very limited as to where money can be spent and it is struggling to treat the vulnerable.

The goal posts seem to change frequently for people who choose nursing or caring as a career. Universities are starting to only accept nurses who are prepared to work to a degree level; soon perhaps it will stretch to honours. This will result in putting more pressure on the social services that provide care.

I personally feel that while anyone can buy a degree, you cannot put a price on lifelong learning. Education is very important but the core of any recovery is receiving compassion and kindness, being actively listened to, and receiving true empathy. These skills are best understood through experience and not by reading a textbook or studying in a classroom. People are individuals and need to be treated as such. We live and learn more from our gut feelings, you learn best from wisdom and experiences. People are not textbooks – they are humans with individual beliefs and needs.

If you want to learn the deeper science then perhaps university is the place to be, but that science is not at the core of nursing. Healing comes from good bedside manners and time spent with individuals and their loved ones. As you get to know someone you build a clearer picture of them, allowing you to make a true assessment of their illness. Shared observations between staff also add to the picture. This was the key to good recovery in my day. People got well far quicker when they were given time to understand the risks and benefits of their treatment, and not just given leaflets as a time-reducing exercise.

People now seem to approach the NHS with the attitude that they are owed a quick fix from it, rather than with the intention of seeking help to fix themselves. Doctors are so fearful of being blamed or sued that they send people to specialists unnecessarily, or over-treat on the demand of the public.

Our bodies are capable of healing themselves; when we get ill it is the body's way of saying, 'Hey! Slow down, you need a break!' But people have become too impatient to wait, too impatient to listen. They put so much demand on others to fix them that the NHS has spent a great deal of money providing freely available help and advice – but how many of these people actually seek out the information or continue to follow through with the advice given?

There was an interesting article in the *Daily Mail* by Nick Boyle, a consultant surgeon, entitled 'Death by Bureaucracy'. Published on the 19th June 2014, it outlined the views of a group of consultants who had all trained at the same time and who were considering leaving the NHS. They were disillusioned, not with being doctors, or the practice of surgery, or with their colleagues or patients, but with an overwhelming sense that they had lost all power over their day-to-day professional lives.

They talked of feeling lost in a sea of bureaucracy over which they had little influence, even going as far as to say that doctors and nurses were in despair. The article also stated that those with managerial roles find that they shoulder an enormous burden of responsibility but have little authority. I was reassured that it was not only NHS nurses feeling the strain from the bureaucracy within the NHS.

Nick Boyle identified a large part of the problem as being because of non-clinical management in the NHS, claiming that 'a lack of clinical leadership literally costs lives'. There are more managers than consultants in the NHS, which results in a massive increase in bureaucracy and targets being set based on government policies rather than from clinical necessity. He goes on to say, 'Put doctors and nurses back in charge of our health service. There are volumes of empirical and academic evidence that without the leadership of these two groups of front-line staff, hospitals fail.'

This huge amount of bureaucracy and unnecessary layers of management dramatically increase the cost of the NHS, diverting increasingly sparse resources away from front-line services.

Another article, in the *Independent* this time, noted a concern that the NHS would soon have to start charging patients £10 a night for the 'hotel costs' of staying in hospital if the financial crisis was not addressed. NHS Confederation chief executive Rob Webster was quoted as saying, 'If the NHS cannot afford to fund everything, then it will need to make tough choices about what it does fund'.

I believe that we are all able to do our bit, and that we must try to do our bit, to improve the future for ourselves and our families. If someone were unfortunate enough to suffer a heart attack, the ripple effect is enormous. The list below, collated by student nurse Rachel Smith in 2015, describes the people who are physically and emotionally affected, as well as those who you would rely on to help you recover. Also listed are some examples of where the NHS spends money. Note this list is not exhaustive and covers one person only:

- The person who discovers you.
- The people who answer the call in the call centre and who arrange the ambulance.
- The emergency staff in the ambulance who give first aid assessment and treatment.
- Staff at the hospital awaiting your arrival who have to get a team together and make theatre ready.
- Other members of the medical team such as scrub nurses, night nurses, anaesthetists, surgeons, phlebotomists, radiologists, the blood transfusion team.
- Unseen staff, which may include porters, cleaners, laundry workers and chefs.
- Medical equipment, such as IV tubing, IV fluids, IV medication, special monitoring machines, oxygen, gases, breathing equipment, dressings.
- Dieticians, physiotherapists, occupational therapists, speech and language therapists, the Mental Health Team, the Investigation and Assessment Liaison team.
- Money must also be spent on items such as beds, laundry, furniture, hoists, slings, commodes, and hand sterilisers.

The emotional cost:
- Family lifestyle change.
- Cost of travel of ongoing follow up appointments.
- Job worries.
- Income worries.
- Childcare worries.
- Homecare availability.
- Aids and equipment for the home.
- Family relationships.
- Family pets.

As you can see, there is a lot to think about, and a lot that can be prevented if action is taken to take care of your health.

You may now be asking what you can do to improve your own health. Well, we need to go back as far as the day you were born to get you thinking about this for yourself.

To understand the development of good health we need to take a look at our own birth. We must consider the time we were born, the place we were born, the family we were born into, the first moment we see the light. Trace back your own journey and learn to understand how you got to where you are today.

Birth was the first traumatic experience you survived, but you were not alone. You did it with a companion – your birth mother – and perhaps a whole team of medical staff. Your experience of being born is not necessarily the same as others. Due to the vibrations you felt from the outside world before you left the womb of your mother, your story will be different. Your mother's inner vibrations, experienced as you were grow-ing in her womb, will be different. Your journey from concep-tion to birth will be different. We are not all born in the same year, at the same time, on the same day, to the same family, or the same community or country; we may not all be our birth mother's first child or our guardian's first child.

One thing we have in common is that the person who we are born or given to will be the first person to have an influence on our emotional programming. Imagine yourself as a new computer waiting for external input – without input the computer will not have a clue what to do. What you think today has been programmed into you by others you have come into contact with. In terms of beliefs, it's worth considering what is your own and what has been adopted. Are your fears your own? Have you arrived at them from hearing other people's fears? We are all programmed to a certain extent by what we see, hear, smell, taste, touch and feel inside (our sixth sense).

Our genes (a unit of inheritance) are created from our father's sperm burrowing into our mother's egg. This means we have a mixture of particular chromosomes. A chromosome is made of protein and a single molecule of DNA, which carries the code that determines our physical characteristics such as facial features, hair colour, body shape, and so on. If you imagine yellow paint representing your mother's egg, and blue paint your father's sperm, then when you mix it together you get green – one part of both parents combining to make a unique, new self.

We are then one body of living energy, with billions of smaller energy balls floating inside us, just like stars in the sky, all fired up and ready for the action called growth. Our organs are operational and working without any instruction from the outside world. However, our conscious brain, which forms our thoughts, is about to be programmed from the information we receive through the senses. It is no wonder that, because we are all born at different times, places, years and into different families, we find it so confusing when we try to connect with or understand other peoples' attitudes, behaviour, beliefs and fears, which we ourselves haven't experienced.

I'm not going to bombard you with in-depth explanations of the developing child and the science that supports it, but I am going to attempt to explain how relationships and the way we communicate is vital to our health and the future development of our children.

We humans continually respond to vibrations. Babies, infants and young children learn from verbal vibrations, visual responses and feelings. Have you noticed that when we speak to a baby we say meaningless things like 'coo coo' and give them a wee tickle, just to get a response? We are gentle and soft-spoken so as not to alarm them; we aim for a smile and not a scream. Have you noticed how babies are automatically able to communicate with a cry when they feel hungry, wet or just want to be held and feel safe? They are not aware of material things, only survival needs, and they don't consider their actions: they just do them. It's their body's normal survival reaction.

As children grow up it's not only what we say to these innocent wee individuals that matters, but how we say it. The tone of your voice, your facial expressions, your ability to comfort them and talk to them, actively listening to them, are all important. Water, food, shelter and warmth from the love you feel and show towards them are the only basic needs they require at this stage to develop healthy brain pathways.

A healthy developing child soaks up information from their senses like a sponge. They copy all you say or do and have a 'monkey see, monkey do' attitude. They will believe all they are told. Your child's blank canvas thus builds up pictures with feelings attached to them, which have been programmed from the outside world. They are no longer purely themselves, they now store mixed messages of everything that has come from those around them.

This input will automatically be stored far beyond childhood into adulthood. Memories of both good and bad things, as well as perhaps confused and distorted experiences, can be stored and retrieved many years later in all sorts of ways. As mentioned in a previous chapter, almost anything can trigger a specific memory, such as the smell of food, perfume, flowers, music, or something you see in a film. Whether this memory is good or bad, it will cause a chemical reaction inside your body.

Imagine for a moment that your head is a big plastic bin where all your life experiences are stored. Every time you experience or learn something new the information will first register in the brain and then go into the store. This information may lie there in your bin for years; you may not be aware that fear, sadness, trauma, or hurt is lying there. The more items you store the more squashed the contents will be, full of all the things that someone has said in the past, or done to you.

As the years go past the bin almost fills to the brim with collected information. The squashed items get pushed deeper down into your bin, rotting away the lining, and soon the bin begins to crack and things seep out the sides. The lid blows off like an uncontrolled explosion as there is no room for more. Things inside are all mixed up, muddled, and the required information can't be found in a hurry. This causes frustration, anger. You become sluggish as the system clogs up and the body bends over with the weight of everything you carry.

The only thing left to do is to clean the bin out, just like cleaning out a garage, bedroom or house. To help restore your body you will need to throw out rubbish you no longer need from your bin, but there is so much stored there it is difficult. Sometimes there is so much in the bin that it overwhelms people, and they find themselves avoiding others as it's the only way they can think of to prevent more information going into the bin.

Whichever way you see fit to de-clutter your brain of all the past rubbish, find a way and your body will start to recover and create new pathways. If you want a new beginning in life start with a fresh, empty bin. As adults we are in total charge of what we choose to store and choose to throw away. If you want to remain healthy you need to have a good clean out now and again and rid your body of old useless toxins, old beliefs, old behaviours and excuses. However, be warned – when you look back at your own growth path and decide to make changes you might discover that your self-improvement plan uncovers some unwelcome issues in your life.

Many people have discovered that the biggest improvement from this approach is that they see relationships with new eyes. Either they view people as truly supportive and appreciate them even more than they used to, or they discover some people just don't seem to have their best interests in mind, and were holding them back with their negative thoughts and degrading comments.

If you're stuck in an unhealthy rut and decide to change your lifestyle by jogging or walking each day, if your partner or friend is not on the same mindset as you are, then you'll probably begin to notice some 'feedback'. This may come from your drinking buddy, eating partner, or your partner in an inactive and non-nurturing lifestyle. If so, there are a couple of things that you may become aware of. You may be both co-dependent, sharing dependencies.

In a toxic relationship the partner feels threatened by your need to change and criticizes your improvements. They may pile negative statements on you, discouraging your every step, laughing and telling you that it won't last. They will continue to bring home all of your favourite junk foods *even after you ask them not to*. They may invite friends round for a drink and encourage you to indulge, or be manipulative, or bully you. These people are often jealous and feel threatened at their own insecurities. They become controlling individuals and may go out of their way to make you fail.

Negative, toxic relationships can cause a person to become physically, emotionally, mentally, and spiritually unwell – dis-ease. They can be draining and abusive. Believing the negative words and thoughts can cause internal injuries that last long after the relationship has ended. Comments and opinions from others get into your brain, just waiting to be recovered if similar situations recur.

It is not easy to distance yourself from toxic people, especially if they are your own relations, but it is necessary to avoid them for your own health and wellbeing. The problems caused by dysfunctional families are related to co-dependency in adults, which basically means a 'relationship addiction', where one person's habits become the other person's problem. The person who is not functioning properly relies on the other person as their medicine, while the person who has become the medicine eventually becomes frustrated and angry because they have tried to fix a partner who doesn't realise they need fixing. Co-dependence is not love, it is need. Love is being free to be yourself, with both parties respecting each other's needs. Balanced energy flows back and forth with the understanding that each is one whole person. Co-dependent people need the other to make them whole.

We humans need to be seen, valued, appreciated and accepted for who we are. One man who came to me for a life-coaching session described his childhood as like living behind a one-way mirror. He said:

Most of the time I feel like I'm out of the picture. My family just don't see me, they only see me when they want something from me, and it makes me feel like an object that they can pick up when I can be of use and ignored when their needs are satisfied. Most of the time I feel like I'm nothing more than material object.

Many of us are so preoccupied with ourselves that we don't see the people around us until something tragic happens. I've heard this compared to being like a sports coach who sits on a bench watching the game from a distance. He is off the field and can see everything that needs tweaking to get the best performance from the players. If you're playing then you have no vision of what's around you, you can't see the improvements you need to make when you are running about involved in the game. You can't be sure what the other person will do or how they will do it. You can't see what the coach can see because you're in the game. It's only when you take a step back to reflect on your own performance, perhaps by watching a recording of the game, that you are able to make changes.

In time people do change but only if they want to, and for reasons of their own, so it's important to realise that if you want change to occur then the only person you can change is yourself. So often I hear of people staying in relationships for the wrong reasons. Sometimes it's a fear of being alone, or they might feel too old to start over, or it might just be a case of the better the devil you know than the devil you don't. It is very sad to hear people put limits on their own personal growth for fear of what their partner might do or say to them. You will never truly be happy if you're not free to fulfil your true potential.

Although many marital vows promise staying together 'till death do you part', it could be possible that they really mean the death of a relationship. In any relationship, be it with family or colleagues through marriage or friendship, there may come a time when you feel that you have more to offer. You may experience the magnetic pull that guides you towards your true potential and purpose in life. To deny yourself this opportunity would be a great loss, both to you personally and to the world around you, and may be the cause of some future illness.

All too often I've heard people saying when something tragically goes wrong that it was the wake-up call they needed to help them turn their lives around. The decision to better our lives regularly seems to follow some dreadful or fearful experience, which makes me wonder if perhaps that is just the way the universe has planned it for us. Perhaps all the trauma and drama is meant to happen as a lesson, and if we learn from every experience, good or bad, we will have something that helps us to get to the next level in our spiritual growth.

I believe that relationships come and go for a reason; they are built on trust and common ground. When the common ground changes, so will the relationship. If you let your relationship become a habit you can't shake off then your personal growth will be compromised and so will your relationship with the other party. It is better to have a good relationship with yourself first so you can grow to your full potential. Any successful relationship needs a partner who is willing to grow with you, so you are able to maintain good health and wellbeing.

Chapter 6

What side of the bars are you on?

*"Stress can break your body; bullying can kill
your spirit."*

Stress has become very common and, like many scientists and researchers, I believe it is this century's main cause of chronic illnesses.

When working closely with families I came to understand the stress that people endure in their lives, whether it comes from poor relationships, money issues, loneliness, depression or illness. Stress can start early in childhood and get progressively more serious because children don't understand how to deal with it. It might begin with something as simple as a fear of the dentist, doctor, hospital or exams, which can all be felt in the gut or show up as a headache. The effects of stress all come under the same umbrella of anxiety and insecure feelings. In fact, any unprepared-for events that cause feelings of insecurity can change the chemistry of the cells in your body, whether you're a child, teenager or adult. Even the smallest of things can powerfully affect emotions when we are young, and for many of us the pain carries over to the current day.

In a few years time it may be your own children growing up with such memories. Our job as parents is to provide them with as many fond memories as possible, which will fill them with the happy cells necessary for a balanced brain full of functional pathways. It has been reported that infantile stress has increased in the last decade. There are suggestions that the modern family structure, with its reduced interaction between parents and their children, may be responsible. Mothers may not be aware of just how important their role is when they decide to be a parent, and both children and adults can find it very difficult to cope with each others demands. Looking back at our grandparent's and great grandparent's relationships it can be easily understood why many of us behave like we do today.

I strongly believe that prolonged stress is one of the major contributing factors to negative changes in our immune system, the infection-fighting system. I also believe that if we could reduce stress in our lives then our bodies would recover and much chronic illness, sleeping problems, cancer, obesity and many more debilitating illnesses such as multiple sclerosis, rheumatoid arthritis, and dementia would be a thing of the past.

To better understand the effects of stress on the body, it might help to imagine a narrow bridge built over a small river. The bridge was designed to carry small vehicles like motor-bikes or perhaps the occasional car and is strong enough to cope with such a daily load. However, a larger vehicle might sneak across now and again, placing the bridge under a little more pressure for a while. The bridge might shake a little but quickly recovers once the larger vehicle has passed.

Then imagine that a lorry comes along, just managing to

squeeze through with a hair to spare at each side. The bridge feels the pressure and starts to shake. Perhaps some bricks become loose. Although it can be easily repaired by a builder filling in the cracks, the bridge becomes weaker.

Now imagine that the lorry takes its shortcut over the bridge every day, month after month. The bridge would soon collapse under the continual stress. It can no longer be repaired; it must now be entirely rebuilt. The damage could have been avoided if people had stuck to the limits of the bridge.

The human body can only stand up to so much pressure before it experiences signs of collapse such as back ache, headache, joint pain, or breathing difficulties. If we do not listen to the messages our body gives us and act to reduce the stress then we inevitably collapse under the weight of the pressure. Our brain may think we are coping but our body tells a different story.

I have also noticed a link between illnesses and different types of personalities or family relationship dynamics. People who have very amicable personalities such as those who are unable to say no, or who perhaps lack assertiveness and self-esteem, tend to lean towards co-dependency. These unselfish people commonly suffer from bullying – they supply others with free energy, then before they are aware of what has happened they become tired and drained, just like a dead battery. If they have no way to recharge their battery then they are likely to experience stress and mental illness.

Most bullies suffer from fear and anger, an internal emotional state. Fear can be helpful in some ways as it can motivate us into taking action, but it is separate from the behaviour it might trigger. Fear may make someone feel angry in response to a frustration or injury; if we don't like something that has happened we may choose revenge. We use anger when we want to correct something that we think is unfair.

Aggression is usually the result of anger. It is an attacking action that takes many forms, including verbal insults, physical punishment, threats and sarcasm. Instrumental aggression presents as cold and calculated and aims to get some reward, hostile aggression seeks to hurt someone, while annoyance aggression looks to annoy someone and stop them being an irritant. No matter what the type, it is unhealthy.

Frustration is different from anger. Frustration is the feeling we get when we don't get our own way, or are born into poverty and can't get what we want. It is a response to injustices in our society, to parental restrictions, or to physical injuries that change our way of life. It can also be a response to something as simple as being stuck in traffic when you need to be somewhere.

Our emotions are much the same as a thunder and lightning storm really. Clouds build up when it gets humid, you hear the rumbling of thunder and lightning, then on comes the heavy rain. When we get angry or upset most of us become hot, red in the face and sweaty. Our brain becomes cloudy and we start to lose our self-control. The head thumps like thunder, then like lightning we strike out to release the tension. It's after this that tears, just like the rain, usually begin. Depending on the storm it may rain for some time. In some cases the tears do not appear, leaving feelings of emotional frustration bubbling away inside. In the meantime the storm passes, the sky clears, and the sun comes out. We may not be able to control the real weather but we can change and control the emotional weather inside, and so hopefully avoid hurting either ourselves or someone else.

If we continue to bottle everything up there is a great danger of anger and aggression striking out. That is why so many men find themselves behind bars. When working in the prison I witnessed full-blown blinding rage, the extreme of anger and aggression. Rage can be described as a hurricane or tornado and is a complete loss of self-control. When someone gets to this height it is very frightening. They can be very difficult to bring down as they are totally blind to their surroundings. They kick, bite, scratch and punch, using all their survival instincts to get free. I have seen more than ten strong men, in riot gear, trying to physically restrain one single person in a hurricane rage.

So, how do we learn to control our anger? How do we learn to avoid aggression? How can we learn to forgive others? How can we forgive ourselves?

Simple: humans have unlimited potential when we consciously choose to work on our own personal growth. It's our choice, it's up to us to take charge of our own direction in life. It takes only one small change to have an impact on the people and world around us.

It's like throwing a stone into a calm lake and watching the ripple stretch far and wide. One small change can change your world. I strongly believe change is possible for most humans.

We all have delicate cells and chemicals in our body and if they are not synchronised there will be unbalanced chaos. It is this imbalance that eventually develops into chronic illness.

What is interesting is that most people will have their own way of releasing built-up tension – some in healthy ways like jogging and going to the gym, creating art, reading, listening to music, or socialising over a coffee, while some may choose unhealthy solutions like smoking, gambling, drinking, or sitting for hours playing computer games. Not many people take notice of their own bodies until they become ill; not many people understand how their own bodies work. They may know the ins and outs of their mobile phones, computers or cars, but they have never found time to take an interest in themselves. Our bodies are fascinating and we are all solely in charge of our own one. We all seem to look to others to fulfil our needs, but the truth is that all you need is right inside you. To be completely free from illness you just need to learn to love yourself, be true to yourself, be kind to yourself, be selfish to your self.

If you have been fortunate enough to fly on a plane, you will remember the safety instructions given before the flight takes off. They stipulate that in an emergency you should place your own oxygen mask over your nose and mouth before helping others. If you don't take care of yourself first you would be no use to anyone; you would simply pass out.

Our bodies are amazing

There is a whole other world going on in our bodies that most most of us don't know anything about. There are more cells in our body than stars, and they don't know you even exist. They are just inside your body doing a job. They have a brain of their own and respond to the input received by every thought, feeling and action, which are delivered by electrical impulses shooting various signals through our spinal cord, just as you would see a shooting star in the night. These electrical impulses send messages to all parts of the body; therefore everything you do will have an effect on the electrical power station in your brain.

The world and human existence mirror each other: the sun lights up the world every morning just as humans rise out of bed, when the weather gets cold we get cold, when the sun doesn't shine then our mood is dull. For everything that goes on in the world there is a reaction at the human level. Everything is connected. As our bodies react to what we see, hear, smell, taste, touch and feel, signals are sent to the brain to alert the cells, allowing information to filter through our systems and protect our inner world from harm.

All noise vibrations from the external world seep through our ears to our inner world, causing a related internal reaction. If we hear calming music or soft-spoken voices it will make us feel good and relaxed, but if we hear loud voices or thundery noises it may cause us to feel fear. If the loud noise is constant and repetitive then our cells build up tension and become overwhelmed. An electrical current sparks off and, like thunder and lightening, flashing occurs inside our brain as messages are passed from one neuron to the next.

The air that surrounds us is sucked into our inner world as we breathe in through our nose and out through our mouths. If we breathe slowly we are relaxed, but if we breathe fast, not allowing air to fully circulate inside before it exits again, we may find ourselves in a panic.

Imagine your heart as the sun, bright and warm. It is always glowing and pumping energy all round our inner world, but when the sun is not so bright (as so often in Scotland) it reduces the energy flow to all parts of your inner world and makes you feel down. Our mood tends to match the weather and seasons; as we get older and have less energy, the winters feel longer. When young and full of energy we tend not think much of the weather or seasons as we're fired up with the anticipation of new things and experiences.

Your stomach is like a food factory where food is stored until the inner chemistry gets to work on it, squeezing out the goodness and then soaking the rest in acid, churning it into thick liquid. It is then sent to the small intestine, where food nutrients soak through the lining villi into the blood, stopping off at the liver for sorting before proceeding round the rest of your body. The large intestine gets to work with the leftovers, squeezing it down to the outside world.

Our kidneys clean the blood, taking around four minutes to turn the waste and water into urine, after which it is stored in the bladder. The muscles around the bladder keep things at bay until the floodgates send messages via the spinal cord to your brain asking the guard to direct you to the loo. If the message is slow in getting there then... oops!

Our veins and arteries rely on their connection with the heart and lungs. Veins are a one-way street for blood to travel along. Blood flows away from the heart to the lungs for oxygen, then returns to the heart via arteries. The arteries carry oxygen around the body; once it has completed the cycle it will meet up at branches called capillaries, where cells absorb the oxygen through capillary walls. Once the arteries have delivered oxygenated blood to all systems they meet up again with the veins, which carry blood back to the lungs to pick up yet more oxygen.

There are many organs in our body and they all require our love and attention, otherwise we do not function to the best of our ability. We are not aware of all the work that's being done inside our bodies until we stop functioning properly. We are not separate from our body, we need to look after everything inside to ensure it works for us. If you neglect your body you and those connected to you will suffer.

You may have already heard of the so-called 'happy' chemicals. There are all kinds of different hormones in our body doing different things, but lets focus on the chemicals – dopamine, endorphin, oxytocin, and serotonin – that stimulate your brain. You will find these chemicals in the limbic system, which is surrounded by a huge cortex. Both have their own job to do in keeping us alive. Each chemical motivates us in different ways.

Dopamine helps you to get what you need. It keeps expecting rewards such as food, social interaction and reproduction. It's the most important reward pathway in the brain; it motivates us by giving us pleasurable feelings in return for rewards. It activates pathways and informs the memory centre in the brain to pay attention so it can be repeated in future. It is vital to survival.

Endorphin masks pain when you have sustained an injury and you need to get to a place of safety or help. Morphine is an artificial endorphin. Opiate drugs such as heroin and opium may be potent painkillers, but the human body already has these endorphin chemicals built in, and they switch on and off as required.

Oxytocin is produced through warm emotional contact with another person or animal. It's the feel-good factor when you're around friends, and it helps you to find comfort and safety in companionships and good relationships. It is the stress-reducing hormone. Scientists who have researched oxytocin now believe that not only is oxytocin related to childbirth and breastfeeding, but it also has an important role in the cardiovascular system, digestive system, and wound healing. Kindness and compassion effectively make us happier therefore oxytocin protects the heart from damage through dilating blood vessels. Oxytocin binds to the receptors on blood vessels, causing the release of another chemical called nitric oxide, which clears the blood vessels of oxidative stress (free radicals) and helps to prevent inflammation, reducing blood pressure. In short, love, compassion, kindness, forgiveness, cuddling and so on, have been scientifically proven to show some powerful anti-inflammatory effects and can even cause physical changes in the brain.

Serotonin is released when you receive respect. It is the security chemical.

If you are familiar with modern alternative therapies you may have heard people speak about the Chakras, the human energy system. If we were able to balance our energy field then we would be on our way towards preventing physical illness such as cancer, heart disease, neurological disease/disorders and psychological disease. In the scientific world these Chakras are known as your endocrine system (see diagram on the following page). They are vital organs that if balanced would save lives.

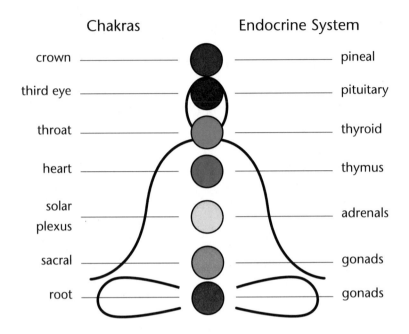

I feel it in my water

Water is our main source of energy. If disruptions occur and are not corrected then our physical body will simply rot away like a polluted river.

Consider the commonly heard phrase, 'What goes around comes around'. To me it means that if you don't treat people right then it will come back to haunt you, that the consequences of your actions will have to be dealt with eventually. When I have felt uneasy about things I have also found myself saying, 'This is not right, I feel it in my water.' I have also heard others say, 'I feel it in my bones.' In my view such statements are an instinctive premonition of what's about to happen, the gut instinct that we all experience occasionally.

We say things to ourselves all the time. Our brain never switches off; there is constant chatter going on. If you're like me then sometimes, when I have done something silly due to lack of concentration, I have a conversation in my head. Most likely I'm trying to excuse myself!

I'm sure we have all said something to someone that we have not been proud of, or that someone has taken what we have said the wrong way. Sometimes things we don't mean to say just slip out. We might try to justify what has happened but it's often a case of making excuses for something we feel embarrassed or ashamed about. How long do such feelings and conversations take before they finally leave our system?

After I started paying more attention to what I was saying I realised that I was using the phrase, 'I feel it in my water', much too often. It made me wonder if perhaps everything is just 'in our water', if perhaps our modern illnesses are simply connected to our water. After all, our body is approximately 75% water, the planet earth around 70% water. We are submerged in a watery substance in our mother's womb to keep us safe. When we are born we rely on water for life; the human brain will not function without water.

Could it be that God is water and the spirit that flows through us all, just as water flows through each and every one of us? If we turn against ourselves we turn against God, the greatest sin of all. If you turn against yourself and behave in a way that provokes fellow human beings into turning against you, then the composition of the water in our body changes, becoming malformed and toxic just like a polluted river. We then suffer the consequences, just as the 'What goes around, comes around', phrase predicts.

We can't get away from water; we rely on it so much in our

everyday lives. Water circulates around the planet just as it does inside our bodies. Earth's water circulates by vapour, rain, snow and ice, while we humans breathe, sweat and cry. When we bottle things up we freeze it somewhere in our bodies. Deep down inside there is old information that eventually defrosts and flows to the surface, leaving our bodies through our eyes as tears. Our faces become red after we cry, leaving our eyes burning and painful, perhaps due to the hot toxic water that's been stored for so long in our subconscious. We always feel better after we cry, again because we're getting rid of that toxic water from our body.

We rely on water for many of our daily recreational activities. It helps us to relax, we bathe in it, swim in it, children have fun splashing in rain puddles, we enjoy walking by seas and rivers, we like looking at fountains, we enjoy surfing, kayaking, canoeing, snorkelling, diving, and fishing, we pay vast amounts of money to swim with dolphins. We have more connection with water than we realise.

Water is responsible for our circulatory system, keeping our brain and bodies hydrated so that we can function. It is also widely used in industrial processes and hence keeps the world functioning. It is crucially important for the survival of every human being.

I became very interested in water and started reading as much material as I could get my hands on, hoping to find some validation of my theory about water's connection to our chronic illnesses. This is when I came across Masaru Emoto and his research.

In 1987 Masaru Emoto experienced pain in his foot while at work. One of his colleagues introduced him to a type of water that worked miraculously, relieving the pain. He was so impressed that he began to study water. He was convinced that water took in external information that affected the mind and body. After many years of research and experiments he needed to prove his belief with physical evidence. He came up with an idea after reading a book on the mysteries of science edited by David Savold and Julia Leigh, which inspired him to freeze water and look at the crystals.

He started to take photos of these frozen crystals from water in different countries and the results were all very different. He then carried out an experiment on several bottles of water with positive phrases like, 'thank you', 'happiness', 'well done', or 'love and gratitude' on them. The pictures show beautiful clear crystals. He contrasted this with an experiment on labelled bottles with negative messages like, 'no good', 'you fool', or 'unhappiness'. The photos show very misshapen and cloudy crystals. Masaru Emoto has written many books and they are all worth reading.

If we were to practice being kinder to one another then we could change the shape of the water flowing through us, reducing inflammation and negating the greatest cause of pain. I went on to read many other books and they all seemed to be sending out a similar message. We should encourage people to laugh and cry, balancing those hormones and ridding our bodies of toxic water.

Chapter 7

The GAPLEGS model

*Seven reasons why we should conquer
the 7 deadly sins*

I have developed the GAPLEGS model as a tool to develop awareness of how ill heath manifests itself. It is based on the seven deadly sins of Greed, Anger, Pride, Lust, Envy, Gluttony and Sloth (GAPLEGS).

Greed

Greed results in pain. Greedy people are arrogant and self-centred; they think they have a passport to success and believe money will buy them anything. While they don't mind standing on people to get ahead, it means that they are the ones who will fall the furthest. They will not have done anything that benefits their true self, or other people in the world. They are often deprived of true love because they are attractive to people who lack in confidence. Money is their safety net, money gives them the happy chemicals. However, these people who can't share will be remembered for their greed – just like Scrooge.

People who fit into this group are often gamblers, worka-holics and cheaters, and are highly competitive. They may also have an addiction compulsion.

Greedy people are self-centred and avoid spending money on their family, even though they can clearly afford it. They will come up with all sorts of excuses to opt out of family holidays as they grudge the cost of hotels, meals out and travel. They value personal material objects like an expensive car over sharing quality time with the family. This can cause many relationships to end.

Anger

As discussed before, people get angry for many reasons. Out-bursts of anger are caused by a lack of self-control in the face of frustration. A loss of freedom can result in 'neurological rage', which we often see in prisons. Neurological impairment is caused in childhood due to life trauma or brain injury. The front part of the brain, the frontal lobe, is the conscious thought part of the brain and does not develop properly if it has been damaged. Problems in the frontal lobe can result in regular mood changes.

Pride

Pride comes when you do something wrong and make any excuse to avoid owning up to it. Pride is a delusional, false belief state. Pride is not the same as dignity – dignity means respect. Pride can be a devastating emotional cause of distress and very destructive to our health and wellbeing. Prideful people are hypersensitive, they may become extremely pre-occupied with themselves and can become very bitter, resent-ful of people who seem to succeed. In school these people are probably outstanding in class and the centre of attention. However, when they get into the bigger world they become aware that they are not as great as they first thought. Proud people tend to be cruel and are more than capable of bullying. They will also be reluctant to help others out, even when they are struggling. These people may have forgotten their humble beginnings; they can become very isolated due to their ego-centric nature and will refuse help at all costs.

Lust

Some may think lust is love, which is the hardest lesson of all to learn. Lust can be a painful, soul-destroying feeling that leaves many with a broken heart. For young lovers entering into their first relationship lust can be a devastating experience that rips through the Chakras like a tidal wave. Once you have succesfully navigated your way through childhood the first challenge is to avoid the destruction that lust can bring. Lust is a magnetic feeling that attaches you to another human being. At first it consists of a sensual attraction between both parties. However, this lust will wear off, as once the happy chemical dopamine is satisfied it returns to a normal state. This is what makes lust unlike true love, where two people share trust and encourage each other's interests, helping each other to grow. Lust is in the moment self-gratification, which continues until people find that their other needs are not being looked after. Electric feelings wear off and either party may look for a new relationship with no commitments.

Another danger of lust is that it can cause us to be reck-less, and with no time to consider protection many people end up conceiving on the first night of a lustful attrac-tion. Unrestrained sexual desire can destroy all hopes and dreams, causing enormous emotional pain, guilt, blame and shame.

Envy

People who become envious of others feel pain when someone else has something they want, whether it is an object, money or a new house. It could be that the envious person wants the status others have. Childhood envy begins when the child has been compared unfavourably to other siblings.

I have often heard comparisons discussed within families. One common example is a mother commenting that X is not as good at maths as Y. Another common complaint is that Y was a baby that cried a lot, and that if the mother had Y first she might not have had another child. When our value as an individual is judged by others, feelings of worthlessness and unfairness can arise. These are borne out in irrational behaviour. No one likes to be compared to other people's standards as it feels like an attack on our own values. Children absorb such comments and they become embedded in their feelings. Later in life they may become envious of others' successes.

I'm sure we have all had the occasional pang of envy. I certainly did at school. I was envious of people who did not have to study to get good grades, as I studied hard and got nowhere. For most people, these pangs of envy pass quite quickly. However, for the envious person they do not pass, and they can cause feelings of rage. It can also drive people into debt as they continually try to get bigger and better things. This distorted attitude and behaviour can dominate people's lives.

Gluttony

Food in this day and age, in Great Britain, is in abundance and is often an indulgence. Food is easily found; we lust over TV commercials, which constantly bombard gourmet food demonstrations at us. In the bookshop and newsagent shelves we have thousands of cookbooks and magazines devoted to saturating ourselves with eating and drinking. Not only has this contributed to poor physical health, it has also had undesirable effects on our emotional health. Many millions of people today are unable to live a fulfilled life as they obsessive over counting calories, dieting, binging, and starving, all of which cause food-related anxieties. People in all walks of life think constantly about food every moment of the day.

I once spoke to someone who spent three hours shopping for just one meal. They looked at everything on the label – calories, sugar, salt, fat – and worried that they were becoming a slave to food. They had been told by a dietician of the dangers to their health if they did not pay close attention to food labels and it had ended up becoming an unhealthy obsession.

Gluttony has become a major factor in chronic illnesses throughout the world, often not helped by the habit of counting calories rather than quality nutrients. Eating non-nutritional food is setting yourself up for disaster. Many eating disorders stem from an unfulfilled emotional void that results in low motivation. We then tend to turn to the quick fix release of happy chemicals that eating brings. Our society has more restaurants than gyms; we are a nation of coffee shops, cake shops, fast food chains. They are everywhere – garden centres, retail parks, supermarkets, pubs. We eat because we can and not because we need to. Our poor bodies are out of shape, our lungs are out of breath, our arteries are clogged up and people are making great profits while encouraging us to indulge.

Sloth

Sloth is the loss of a sense of meaning, and it is associated with guilt, worthlessness, despair, hopelessness and a loss of direction. It is the breaking down of deep emotional bonds and causes ruptured families, indifference to the welfare of others, physical laziness, deep sadness and sorrow. People can sometimes give up due to feeling that the efforts they make may not have had the broad social impact they hoped for. They may become bitter individuals and hide away from the rest of society.

If we could avoid the seven aspects of the GAPLEGS model then our physical and mental health would increase significantly. The world has more to offer if we are healthy enough to enjoy our time here. Living daily with chronic illness and constant disappointment is really a living hell.

There is a point to all the suffering, however. We will not be able to evolve into the next life if we have not learned from this life. My belief is that a lesson is being taught through pain. It teaches us to return to innocence and detach ourselves from the things that have upset us in the past, to detach from our unhealthy connections to things with no human value. We must see the past as a learned experience and return to the time we were just a blank sheet with no input from other people's belief systems. It is much healthier to trust your own gut feelings than to be influenced or brainwashed by other people's beliefs, which often only reflect other people's shortcomings. Trust in the wisdom you have gained from your own experiences, take the time to be still, and invest in your own thinking and personal growth. If we all stood very still and quiet I wonder what we would be able to hear. It is hard to imagine, but it may be just the key to recovery and what is needed to allow our bodies to heal and the brain to make new pathways.

I also believe that meditation is the medicine of tomorrow, but you will not get it from the chemist; meditation is free to all who believe in its benefits. Meditation seeks to control the chattering in your head with an awareness of yourself. Mindfulness meditation is about returning to innocence and finding a new beginning away from what you have learned in the past, that which will not work for you in the present.

Mindfulness meditation is about letting go of yesterday and being right in the moment, being aware of every breath, not anticipating the future. Mindfulness is about controlling your own thoughts. It is a way of paying attention and being aware of what is happening in our lives, noticing how things make our bodies feel, being aware of our thoughts and their effects. Being in a mindful state helps us recognise our unconscious emotional and physiological reactions to our habits. It takes practice but it does encourage your brain to repair itself and develop new pathways for information.

Imagine that the brain is like a spaghetti junction with roads going in all directions. If there are roadworks going on we have to find an alternative route, but in the meantime everything comes to a standstill. It will now take longer to get to our destination and we become frustrated and anxious. This frustration has an effect on the inside of our body. Mindfulness allows us to identify that effect and become aware of what it is doing to us, which allows us to act on the information and reduce stress.

Chapter 8

Are we all trapped behind bars?

"Truth may be painful to digest, but facing it will set us free."

As mentioned previously, I am very passionate about the elderly and work closely with them professionally. I'm sure some must be very angry after the emotional battles they have fought, suffering through war and all the family separation it caused. To go through everything they have and end up as prisoners in their own home for fear of being abused by our younger generation must be awful. Their losses are shameful; when moving into care homes some have to give up their pets, while some even have to sell their own homes to afford it.

Living with my grown-up family is not what I expect when I get older. I encouraged my children to be strong enough to fly the nest and go on their own journey, learning from their new experiences. I hope that I am respected for being their mother, and I hope they recognise that I did the best I could with the knowledge I had at the time.

Everyone needs a purpose in life. My purpose is to be available for my family until the day I can no longer make meaningful choices. I am the one they can fall back on and trust when they are confused. When I get older, I want to be able to stay in my own home for as long as I can. I don't want to be wrapped up in cotton wool in case I fall and break a leg. I will take responsibility, swallow my pride, and get a walking stick or wheelchair if need be – whatever helps to keep me independent and safe. I certainly don't wish to be forced to sell my own home so I can enter a private care home that I have little choice in deciding upon.

I strongly believe that we shouldn't expect something for nothing – life's journey is far more enjoyable if you have a strong sense of self-achievement, if you experience the feeling of being in control of your own path. I believe we are all able to do our bit, and we must try to do our bit, as otherwise the future of the human race will be bleak.

Local councils and health and safety fears have done a lot to encourage people not to be self-sufficient or to take care of themselves. When I was young whole families would gather at the seafront in Aberdeen to listen to music at no cost; Union Terrace Gardens had free entertainment every summer and neighbours would take care of your children with no expectation of financial reward. Now nearly everything has a cost. Our lack of freedom has cost the government a fortune on health and social care as we have been forced to go against our human instincts. Life was much simpler back in the seventies. Our children have become so over-protected that they are now confined to their room playing computer games and are not allowed to get dirty for fear of germs.

Not so long ago I was on a child's school outing when one of the boys spotted a frog. He was about to stand on it so I picked it up to show it to the children, and of course to prevent it from a sudden death. I was immediately shouted at by a senior member of staff who literally screamed at me to put it down. Heaven only knows what that taught the children. I nearly wet myself and thought I was about to be attacked! I was immediately given hand sanitiser to clean my hands. We only used to wash our hands before eating a meal, and I definitely hadn't planned on eating the frog. In my day nature was encouraged but now we teach our children to be scared of it.

We live in a country that people from all round the world flee to for their own safety. They don't come for healthcare or to steal our houses, they come because they are faced with horror, death and torture at home. Most immigrants would love to stay in their own country, at home, if they could. Sometimes I imagine what it would be like if our own government turned on us. Where would we flee to? How far would we go to protect our children and loved ones? While Great Britain has its troubles, at least we are generally safe and can sleep at night in comfort, free from mass terror. Our elderly know well what that feels like.

What you are is not the same as who you are. We all view and experience things in different ways. We may not be all the same, but we are all important, and we have all been given a part to play in this world. Life is just like a computer game we play to win. However, unlike in a computer game, in real life there is no way to cheat without feeling the pain. You have to go through everything, and behind every move there is a lesson to be learned.

In the game of life we grow and change together. I call this game of survival 'human connections'. It is like a giant jigsaw; we all hold a piece of the puzzle, and all we need do is find out where we fit in so we connect to the next piece. This is the plan of evolution.

I suggest we all take a good look at ourselves and be mindful of everything that is going on around us. Appreciate what we have and not be resentful of what we do not have. How great would it be for all of us to live in a society full of acceptance and understanding? This may just be possible if we all practice mindful compassion with each other. Holding on to anger, fear and resentment is not good for your health. It will change your chemistry and make you ill at ease. Let's get together, do something now, and aim for a win-win solution.

You may feel trapped like those patients behind bars, or it may be difficult to decide what side of the bars you are on. You may feel rubbish most days and wish you were in a better situation. Just do the best you can for yourself, and try to change your own regime.

A prayer for good health

We are all at different ages and stages that cause us bother
We have all had different experiences so be patient with your mother
The journey will be varied for each and every one
The important thing to remember is to try and make life fun.

Do not look back in anger, regret or fear of face
Be happy with what you have and accept with loving grace
Play your part with truth and courage no matter how big or small
It's enough you took an active part and you gave to it your all.

Love your neighbour like yourself and free yourself from strife
Be careful how you use your words they can kill just like a knife
Praise the lord whenever you can he loves to hear your voice
If you want a carefree life then prayer is another choice

Pray for all those vagrants who truly like to roam
Pray for all our soldiers who are far away from home
Pray for children everywhere that they may safely play
Pray for each and every one who helps us through the day

Many roads you will want to travel, you may even go astray
If you find you've lost your path all you need do is pray
For God is love and truly kind he will show you new direction
He will not judge or bear a grudge but guide you through correction.

Help to save a life

I have prepared a small checklist that may help you to start changing your regime. It's the small things that can make the biggest difference, things that each one of us can do every day. These will help to make positive changes in your own health as well as in the health of others. Pick one, do it all week, then build on it by picking another.

- Smile

- Always be polite and say thank you

- Give someone a hug

- Say something nice to a person you speak to.

- Open a door for someone

- Don't take personally anything that's said against you

- Don't make assumptions. Be brave and ask questions so you are clear about what something means.

- Avoid gossip

- Call someone or write a letter to someone you haven't seen for a while

- Be patient

- Speak quietly and slowly

- Look at what you have and be grateful

- Clean out your wardrobe and give to charity

- Take thirty minutes to relax

- Have a body massage

- Change your hair style

- Call a friend and go for a walk with them.

- Spend a day with one of your children, each in turn if you have more than one. If you don't have children then do the same with a relative.

If you have completed this list then start your own one.

Further reading

Cantopher, T. (2007) *Stress-related-illness*.
London: Sheldon Press.
ISBN: 9780859699716

Ackerman, Robert, J. (1994) *Silent Sons, a book for and about men*.
New York: Fireside Books.
ISBN: 9780671892869

Secunda, V. (1991) *When you and your mother can't be friends*.
New York: Dell Publishing.
ISBN: 9780385304238

Lebow, G., Kane, B., Lebow. I. (1999) *Coping with your difficult older parent*.
New York: HarperCollins Publishing.
ISBN: 9780380797509

Sullivan, K. (2006) *Bullying, how to stop it, a guide for parents and teachers*.
London: Rodale International Ltd.
ISBN: 9781405087766

Hamilton, David R. (2015) *The science of self-love*.
London: Hay House.
ISBN: 9781781801840

Breuning, Loretta G. (2012) *Meet your happy chemicals.*
Inner Mammal Institute.
ISBN: 9781941959015

Emoto, M. (2005) *The true power of water.*
New York: Atria books.
ISBN: 9781416522171

Schimmel, S. (1997) *Seven Deadly Sins.*
New York: Oxford University Press.
ISBN: 9780195119459